AN INT
LOUDSPEAK

C000272259

Other Titles of Interest

AN INTRODUCTION TO LOUDSPEAKERS AND ENCLOSURE DESIGN

by

V CAPEL

BERNARD BABANI (publishing) LTD
THE GRAMPIANS
SHEPHERDS BUSH ROAD
LONDON W6 7NF
ENGLAND

© 1988 BERNARD BABANI (publishing) LTD

First published — November 1988
Revised and Reprinted — March 1991

British Library Cataloguing in Publication Data:
Capel, V.
        An introduction to loudspeakers & enclosure design.
        1. Loudspeakers
621.38'028'2

ISBN 0 85934 201 8

Typeset direct from disk by Commercial Colour Press, London E7.
Printed and Bound in Great Britain by Cox & Wyman Ltd, Reading

Acknowledgements

The Kapellmeister enclosure design was originally published in the July 1987 edition of Electronics Today International. The Author and Publishers of this book would like to thank ETI for their kind permission in allowing the design to be included in this book.

About the Author

His work as an audio, television and radio engineer with several service organisations including that of Philips, gave him a wide experience expanded by his practical and advisory work on large public address systems. As a violinist who has played in several amateur orchestras, he is able to combine the viewpoints of both technician and musician.

His articles have appeared in the technical press for over thirty years, and he is the author of a dozen books on audio, acoustics and related subjects. He now works full time as a writer and audio consultant.

Contents

Chapter 4

Chapter 5

Chapter 1

THE MOVING COIL DRIVER

Nearly all loudspeakers in use today make use of a principle patented as far back as 1898 by Oliver Lodge, and later developed into a workable loudspeaker by Rice and Kellogg, which they patented in 1925. It says much for their design that it has changed only in details and materials used, since then. It is the moving-coil system.

If you have an old loudspeaker lying around, dig it out and take a close look at it. It may be round or elliptical, but whichever it is, the frame or chassis supports a magnet at the back in most cases, although a few have it at the front (Fig. 1)

Cone Surround

The cone is usually made of paper and is fixed around its outer edge to the frame either directly or by means of a flexible roll of cloth, sponge or rubber. The roll can be either a *half-roll out* in which the roll faces outward or a *half-roll in* whereby it faces inward toward the back of the speaker. When the cone is fixed directly to the frame, there are corrugations around the perimeter; these can be of *two sine rolls*, a *single sine roll* or a deeper *accordian pleat*.

The purpose of these are to permit forward and backward motion of the cone while holding it firmly against any sideways movement, but they also have another important function. When the cone vibrates, ripples can spread out from the centre like ripples in a pond when a stone is thrown in. If you observe pond ripples closely, you will notice that if they encounter a hard boundary such as a stone sidewall, they are reflected back across the surface, but if they meet a soft perimeter of reeds grass or mud, they are mostly absorbed and very few are reflected.

In the case of the loudspeaker cone, reflections are undesirable as they produce spurious cone motion that is not in response to any electrical output from the amplifier. So a necessary function of the surround is to absorb and dampen such vibrations thus eliminating reflections.

1

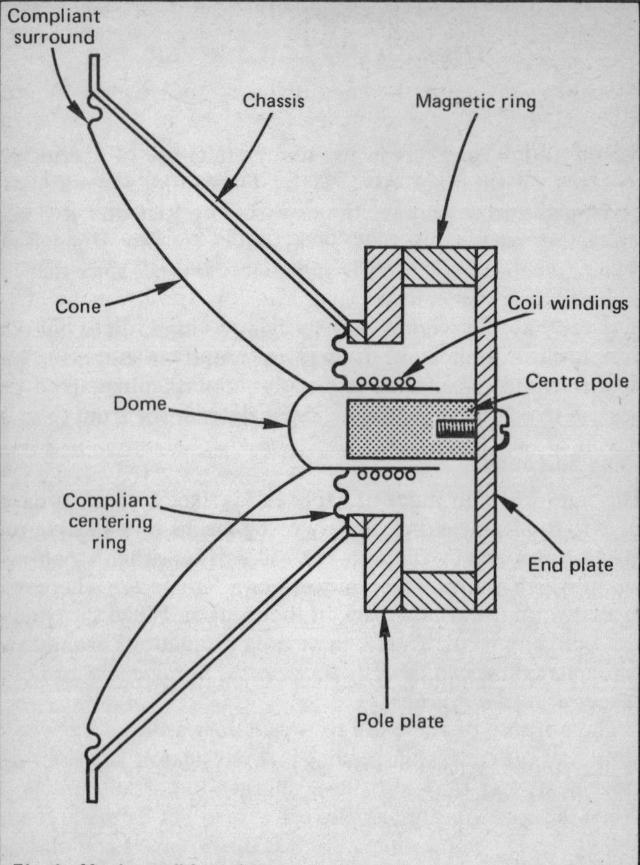
Compliant surround
Chassis
Magnetic ring
Cone
Coil windings
Centre pole
Dome
Compliant centering ring
End plate
Pole plate

Fig. 1. Moving coil bass driver.

Cone Materials

Really, to avoid ripples and flexures which can colour the reproduction even before they may be absorbed by the surround, it is desirable to make the cone as stiff as possible. When a pond surface is frozen hard, ripples, waves or any other disturbances are not possible. Similarly, a perfectly stiff cone would move like a piston, backwards and forwards without any flexures, and so should radiate air pressure waves that are a perfect replica of the electrical currents flowing through the speaker circuit.

So why not make the cone of metal such as aluminium? They have, but that exchanges one set of problems for another. Metal cones tend to 'ring' when subject to vibration, like a bell when it is struck. Most hollow metal cans or boxes give a distinctive sound when flicked with a striker such as a pencil. An ideal loudspeaker cone should have no sound of its own at all, if it has, it will colour the sound it reproduces.

Another problem is inertia. The loudspeaker cone must accelerate and decelerate very quickly in order to produce the very fast vibrations that make up a complex sound wave. To do this its mass must be low. A motor bike will always be away quicker from the lights than an articulated lorry in spite of having a much smaller engine, because its mass is a tiny fraction of that of the lorry. Metal cones, even aluminium ones, are much heavier than other materials commonly used, so they have a disadvantage here too. Honeycombed aluminium is light and about a thousand times more rigid than paper, but has not proved popular.

Polystyrene (same material as ceiling tiles) reinforced with aluminium foil is very light and rigid and has been used. Its snag is poor damping, it has a characteristic sound which is similar to that heard by tapping a ceiling tile held by one hand at its edge.

Bexetrene has been used in many hi-fi speakers being stiffer and more consistent in in its characteristics than paper. It too has poor damping and needs to be coated with a plastic damper to tame it. Polypropylene is a more recently employed material and seems to have advantages as a cone material. It is light, has good self-damping. and is more rigid than paper.

So we come back to paper again. If you tap the paper cone of a loudspeaker, all you hear is a dull plop without any readily identifiable sound. This is the ideal for uncoloured reproduction. It is also very light, so the lack of stiffness is the only major snag. As we shall see later though, in certain circumstances this can be made use of and turned into an advantage.

3

Again it is a remarkable fact that the material which has been used for decades, is still the most widely used and hard to beat in spite of all our modern technology.

The paper pulp stock from which loudpeakers cones are made consists of wood and rag with various additives. One stock commonly used is *kapok*, which is produced from the hollow, oily fibres from the silk-cotton tree. These are especially light and strong and so are well suited for this purpose. Waxes, resins and fungicides are added.

Different characteristics can be imparted to the paper pulp stock by the length of the period for which it is beaten out in vats. Long periods produce short fibres which result in thin hard paper. Cones made from this are light and sensitive, though prone to resonances and poor damping. They are thus more suitable for low-fi transistor radio speakers. Short periods of beating give long fibres, that are more flexible and so less rigid. These are best suited for bass speakers or full-range controlled flexure speakers. It is thus possible to produce a paper for a specific cone application, which is another reason why paper is so popular with the manufacturers.

Cone Resonance

Every physical object has a fundamental resonance, that is a frequency at which vibration is greater than at any other for the same input of energy. Loudspeaker cones are no exception, which means that sound output at the resonant frequency is greater than at all others. The result is an uneven frequency response with an unnatural emphasis at that one frequency.

Below the cone resonant frequency, the sound output falls off at a rate 12 dB per octave, so the frequency response in the bass region is determined to a considerable extent by the resonant frequency which should therefore be as low as possible.

The resonant frequency in free air is proportional to the square root of the reciprocal of the mass of the cone times the compliance of the suspension. The formula is:

$$f_r = \frac{1}{2\pi \sqrt{MC}}$$

in which M is the mass in grams and C is the compliance in metres per newton^{-7}.

Compliance, which is the opposite hence the reciprocal of suspension stiffness, can be calculated from the cone mass and the resonant frequency as follows:

$$C = \frac{1}{(2\pi f_r)^2 \, M}$$

Thus the compliance (the opposite of stiffness) and the mass should be high, but if they are too high other problems can arise. If the suspension is too compliant it may not keep the cone in place at high volume levels; while if the mass is too great, more energy is required to move the cone hence the speaker sensitivity is low and a large amplifier power is needed. The resulting high power dissipation in the coil causes heating with the undesirable effects noted later. Furthermore, as a large mass results in high inertia, the cone will not respond to rapid high frequency electrical signals.

Delayed Resonance

In addition to the resonance due to the effects of mass and compliance there is another. We saw earlier how ripples can move outward from the centre of the cone to the rim and if not absorbed by the suspension are reflected back to the centre. When the cone radius equals one wavelength or a multiple of it, the high and low points of the outward and reflected ripples coincide to produce an apparently stationary ripple or undulation of the cone. It is therefore known as a *standing wave*

However, when the applied electrical signal ceases, the standing wave subsides, and the consequent cone motion radiates sound as it does so. Stored energy is thus released as spurious sound after the cessation of the signal. The effect is thus termed *delayed resonance*. For an 8-inch cone, the fundamental delayed resonance is at 4 kHz with harmonics at 8 kHz and 16 kHz. Efficient absorption by the cone surround is vital to minimise the effect.

Another spurious motion performed by some cones at certain frequencies is what is known as the *bell mode*, with this, opposite quandrants of the cone perform a flapping movement in unison, moving backwards and forwards together while the adjacent quadrants flap in the opposite directions. However, two lines at right angles across the the cone which define the boundaries of each quadrant remain stationary relative to the flapping. This effect is due to lack of stiffness of the cone itself.

The Coil

Continuing our examination of the loudspeaker, we come to the centre of the cone. Here a dome is usually found concealing what lies beneath, and this serves as a dust shield to prevent foreign particles from getting into the air gap and causing grating noises. At certain high frequencies, this dome sometimes moves independently of the cone, by reason of the compliance of the glued joint. It thereby exhibits its own resonant frequency which colours the reproduction. To avoid this in some models, the dome is molded as an integral part of the cone.

Under the dome at the apex of the cone, the coil which consists of a number of turns of copper wire wound on a paper, composition, or aluminium cylinder, is fixed.

To reduce the mass and thereby the inertia in high frequency speakers, aluminium is sometimes used instead of copper wire. To get as many turns as possible within the magnetic field, the wire is often of square, hexagonal, or ribbon configuration instead of round section, thereby saving space, eliminating air gaps between windings, and so permitting more turns per inch. Up to 40% greater conductor density can thereby be achieved, thus making for a more efficient motor system.

The standard impedance of the coil, often termed the *speech coil* or *voice coil*, is 8 ohms, but 4-ohm and 16-ohm models are also available. Formerly, 3-ohms was the standard with 15-ohms for larger units, and these may still be encountered. The impedance consists of resistance and inductance in series, the resistance making up approximately ⅔ of the rated impedance. So the impedance of an unknown speaker coil can usually be determined by adding half as much again to the measured d.c. resistance.

The impedance may be considered a minimum value as it rises to a peak at cone resonance, and is usually above the rated value over most of its frequency range. This is of no importance, but if the impedance should drop below the rated value it could cause overloading of the amplifier. Usually, a higher impedance than that of the amplifier output rating means less power, but often lower distortion, whereas a lower impedance produces higher distortion and possibility of amplifier overload with damage to its output stage. Overloading results in less power being available before drastic distortion sets in. So reduced power results for speaker impedances that are either higher or lower than the amplifier rating, but higher is better and safer.

In multi-speaker systems with complex crossover networks, the total impendance may be mostly reactive at certain frequencies with the result that the output current and voltage are out of phase. Thus high currents may flow at relatively low powers so causing amplifier current-limiting circuits to clip prematurely.

Effects of Heat

Heat is generated in the coil by the current flowing through it, and the resistance rises by some 0.4% per degree C. Modern high-power rated speakers have coils wound on aluminium formers secured by high temperature epoxy resin adhesives and can withstand temperatures up to 300°C. Much lower temperatures are produced at the rated power, but a problem arises with multi-speaker systems. There can be differences in temperature between the bass and treble units due to the different frequency range handled by each, of more than 100°C. Thus there can be a difference of 40% in coil resistance between the two compared to that when cold. Furthermore the difference varies according to the programme. Tonal balance therefore can change during a performance (Fig. 2).

An unexpected result of all this is that amplifiers having large amounts of distortion, such as when operating near their maximum power rating, heat up the treble unit more than low distortion amplifiers. This is because the distortion generated consists of spurious high frequency harmonics which are

Programme	Bass driver	Tweeter
Piano *ff*	100°C	25°C
Orchestra *ff*	150°C	40°C
Heavy rock *ff*	120°C	75°C

Fig. 2. Typical coil temperatures.

reproduced by the treble unit. Now high-power amplifiers are not likely to be operated anywhere near their maximum rating, so we have the seemingly strange result that a low-power amplifier is more likely to overheat the treble-unit coil than a high-power amplifier.

To minimise the effect of heat, various measures are employed to remove it quickly and reduce the temperature build-up. Large magnet assemblies help and sometimes these are blackened and provided with heat fins, but these are long term devices and have little effect on short term temperature variations produced by changing programme content. Treble units being smaller, have a lower maximum temperature than bass drivers, around 120°C. To aid dissipation, some units have gaps between the coil and magnet poles filled with colloidal ferromagnetic fluid held in place by the speaker's magnet. This also slightly increases efficiency and provides a measure of damping.

The Magnet

Returning again to our exploration of the speaker, we find at the back there is a ring of flexible material with corrugations that is secured to the framework at its outer edge and to the cone at its inner. This has the important function of keeping the cone centered relative to the magnet poles. With cheap speakers as used in many transistor radios, the cone can become off-centre due mostly to warping of the thin metal frame so that the magnet poles are not true.

An off-centre cone produces distortion as it rubs against the magnet pole and can be tested for by standing the speaker on its magnet, face upward, and gently pressing the cone inward with the thumbs at opposite points across the diameter, then releasing it. Any rubbing can usually be felt, or heard if an ear is placed close to the cone. Sometimes though, trouble may be experienced from loose coil windings and these may not be detected by this test.

The magnet usually consists of a magnetic ring or rod mounted axially at the back of the speaker. The front pole is terminated by a steel rod pole piece which penetrates inside the coil, and is only slightly of smaller diameter so that the air gap between it and the coil is small. The rear magnet pole is extended by a cylinder or U piece toward the front, where it terminates in a plate with a hole or a ring that surrounds the outside of the coil (Fig. 3).

The magnetic field is thus concentrated between the internal rod and the inside of the surrounding hole and thereby through the coil windings. As with all magnets there is a small external leakage field, but modern speakers are designed to reduce this to a negligible amount. It may seem, when trying to attract a ferrous object with a speaker magnet, that the magnet is weak, but this is the reason. For the same reason there is little possibility of erasing a magnetic tape from the stray field from a modern speaker, this danger is often greatly exaggerated.

Connections from the coil are taken to a couple of soldered blobs on the cone from which highly flexible stranded copper wires connect to a terminal strip on the speaker frame. These wires must never be tight nor must they loop down to touch the cone at any other than their soldered connection; they must be completely free of all obstruction. Failure to ensure this could result in buzzing noises as the cone vibrates.

Dedicated Drivers

To achieve an extended low-frequency response, the mass of the cone needs to be large so that it has a low resonant frequency. Furthermore, its diameter should also be large because the efficiency of the cone falls with decreasing diameter at low frequencies. However, to obtain a good

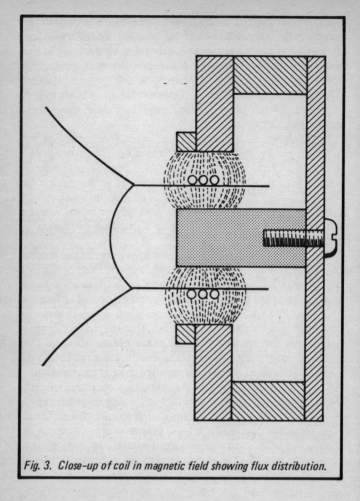

Fig. 3. Close-up of coil in magnetic field showing flux distribution.

transient and high-frequency response the cone should be small and light.

These conflicting requirements have led to the general use of separate drivers for treble and bass, commonly known as tweeters and woofers. The signal is split into two, one containing all the high frequencies and the other the low by a filter circuit termed a *crossover network* and fed to the respective drivers. A mid-frequency range speaker is also used in some models, and some have super-tweeters and sub-woofers to extend the range to inaudibility in the treble and bass.

Disadvantages

One of the disadvantages of having a separate tweeter is that of its physical displacement as a sound source. All high frequencies thereby come from a different point in space from the low frequencies. Several ill effects arise from this.

The resulting sound field does not correspond with that heard by the microphone. Ideally, the sound radiation for each channel should be from a point source, then the stereo positioning can be accurately re-created. To achieve this ideal perfectly is not practically possible, but the aim should be to get it as small as one can. The use of separate drivers enlarges the radiation source and thereby blurs the stereo image.

Another effect is caused by the fact that the cut-off at the crossover frequency is not abrupt but gradual. At and around this point both bass and treble units are handling the same signal. If the tweeter is mounted above the bass unit as it usually is, the output will diminish at points that are higher or lower than the horizontal axis. This is because the difference in distance from each driver to those points delays the sound from the furthest, and so produces partial cancellation (Fig. 4).

A similar effect is due to the bass unit having a much deeper cone than the tweeter. If both are mounted in the same plane, its main radiating area is thus further from the listener than that of the tweeter. At frequencies corresponding to a half wavelength difference, cancellation can be total if both units are radiating the same acoustic energy. Equal radiation can take place only around the crossover frequency, so the effect is greatest when the cancellation and crossover frequencies are actually or nearly the same. So for example, at a depth difference of 2 inches the cancellation frequency is 3.36 kHz. Normally crossover frequencies are lower than this, but partial cancellation will still occur at other values (Fig. 5).

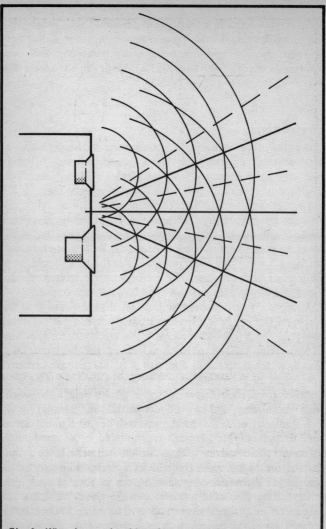

Fig. 4. When bass and treble units are reproducing the same frequency, physical displacement produces radial areas of reinforcement (solid lines) alternating with areas of cancellation (dotted lines). Frequency response thus depends on listening elevation.

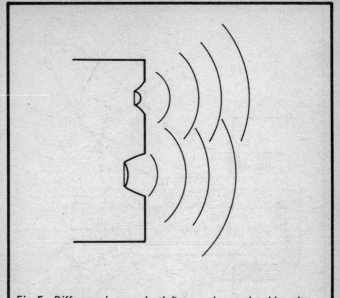

Fig. 5. Difference in cone depth between bass and treble units produce phase differences in frequencies reproduced by both and partial cancellation.

Further disadvantages come from the need for a filter circuit to separate the frequency bands, but we shall deal with these in a later chapter.

Co-Axial Drivers

Some of the disadvantages we have discussed can be avoided or minimised by mounting the tweeter in front of the bass driver. This achieves an effect closer to a point source, but there is still the depth difference and the need for a filter circuit. A separate tweeter supported on struts across the face of the bass unit is one way of achieving this, but a more satisfactory way is to use a co-axial driver (Fig. 6).

This is a speaker having two integral cone systems, the treble within the bass cone. The advantage of this over the use of separate concentric drivers is that the two systems are designed

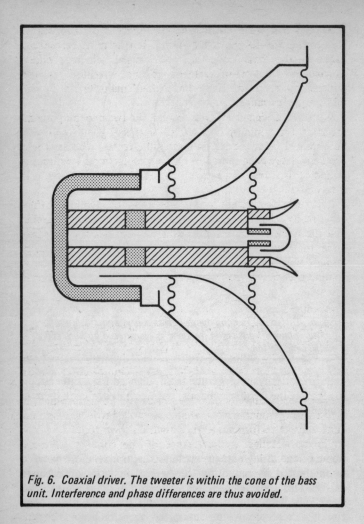

Fig. 6. Coaxial driver. The tweeter is within the cone of the bass unit. Interference and phase differences are thus avoided.

to be compatible, and the treble one is closer to the apex of the bass, so depth difference effect is reduced.

A disadvantage of having an obstruction such as a tweeter unit whether separate or integral, in front of the bass cone is its effect on mid frequencies just below the crossover. An acoustic shadow is cast when an obstructing object is of comparable area to the wavelength of the sound. Furthermore reflections back to the bass cone can be caused which produce cancellation and reinforcement effects. Because of the dimensions involved, these have their main effect in the mid-frequency range.

With well-designed co-axial drivers, the tweeter components are shaped to minimise these effects and very good results can be obtained. However, it is impossible to tell whether these problems have been tamed in any particular model without a period of listening, and if it is then found that they haven't, it is too late!

Early models were not too successful on these counts so they never really became popular. Another more mundane reason is that the more drivers a loudspeaker system has for the same price, the better value it appears to be. So single drivers even though they are two units in one, are less likely to be a commercial success than competitors having separate tweeters.

Controlled Flexure

Using two or more drivers even coaxial ones, to cover the frequency range is not the only answer to the problem, in fact they can create more difficulties than they solve. Now in theory as we have seen, a single speaker cannot cover a wide frequency range, yet in practice they actually do. Single speakers are commonly used for radios and T.V.s in which, if they are of reasonable size and on a suitable baffle, they put up quite a good performance. How then do they do it?

The answer lies in the flexure of the cone at different frequencies. At high frequencies, the central area of the cone responds, but the rest of the cone remains stationary because of its inertia. This independant movement of the central area is possible because of flexure of the non-rigid cone around that area. As the frequency decreases, so larger areas of the cone are brought to play, until at low frequencies the whole cone is in motion (Fig. 7).

This effect occurs to some extent with most speakers, but some cones are specially made to exploit it. These have curved sides, and the flexure points are designed into them so that a

15

Fig. 7. Controlled flexure. At high frequencies the central areas of a curved cone move independently of the rest. The higher the frequency the smaller the active area. This thus serves as an effective high frequency radiator.

smooth coverage of a wide frequency range is achieved. They often have a small horn fixed to the centre of the cone to increase efficiency at high frequencies. Although not having quite the range of separate drivers, it is by no means inadequate, a typical specification being 40 Hz - 17 kHz. Such full-range drivers as they are called, avoid all the problems of having multiple drivers, are closest to a point source and have few vices. They have thus much to commend them.

Cone Velocity and Radiation Resistance

The effect of cone inertia is to limit its acceleration, just as a heavy lorry which has considerable inertia, cannot get away so quickly from the lights as a light car. As the frequency rises and the cone makes more excursions per second its speed needs to increase to maintain the same amplitude. This requires more power, but if the power is constant the speed must also be constant. So when the frequency rises, the amplitude of the cone excursions must decrease to maintain the same speed. This means that the response diminishes as the frequency increases, an effect which without compensation would give a very poor treble reproduction.

Fortuitously, and by one of those rare quirks of the laws of physics, there is another defect in the way sound is propagated by a loudspeaker cone that almost exactly cancels the effect of the first. This is *radiation resistance.* At low frequencies the cone is an inefficient sound radiator. It pushes the air out of the way instead of compressing it into a sound wave.

As the frequency increases, the air does not move aside fast enough to avoid compression but offers a resistance to the cone and so produces sound. The higher the frequency up to a certain point, the greater the radiation resistance and the more efficient the air coupling to the cone. Thus the acoustic output rises and exactly compensates for the diminishing cone excursions.

The compensating effect works up to a point where the radiation resistance is at a maximum and cannot increase further. This frequency range is termed the *piston region* of operation. Above this the response begins to fall off because the cone excursions due to velocity effect continue to decrease. However, cone flexure effects maintain the response further, and also the beaming effect at high frequencies increasingly concentrate the sound in front of the cone. Thus a useful response continues well above the piston region so making full-range single-unit speakers viable.

The piston region transition point is dependant on the diameter of the cone. For a flat disc radiator in a true infinite baffle, the relation between the transition frequency and the cone diameter is:

$$f = \frac{68{,}275}{\pi d}$$

in which d is the cone diameter in centimetres.

Doppler Effect

Doppler effect is frequently heard when an ambulance or police car passes. The number of sound waves reaching a stationary listener in a given time is increased by the forward velocity of the vehicle as it approaches. Hence the frequency is greater and the pitch of the sound heard by the listener is higher. When the vehicle passes and recedes, the sound wave count per unit of time is then reduced by its velocity, and so the pitch drops.

The same effect can be produced by a loudspeaker cone when it is producing a high and low frequency simultaneously. Visualise the cone oscillating rapidly at the high frequency. At the same time it is moving slowly (relative to the high frequency excursions) forward and backward to generate the low frequency.

When the cone moves forward toward the listener, the pitch of the high frequency sound is raised, and when it moves backward, the pitch is lowered. Thus the high frequency tone is modulated by the low, the effect being a form of frequency modulation distortion.

The modulation is proportional to the speed of the cone at its low frequency excursion, just as the doppler pitch change of the ambulance siren is proportional to the vehicle's speed. If it travelled at walking pace the difference would be too minute to be detected.

So the distortion is greatest when the cone is making large bass excursions. Now as small cones must make larger excursions than large ones to generate the same acoustic power, it follows that small cones generate more f.m. distortion. When two different sized speakers are compared, the distortion increase in the smaller one is proportional to the square of the decrease in cone diameter from the larger unit. It is at a maximum for a listener on axis but decreases with the off-axis angle.

Doppler distortion is one argument in favour of having separate drivers for the bass and treble, although in theory it can still occur between widely separated frequencies within the pass band of each unit. Listening tests though, suggest that a

20 mm cone excursion is the lower limit below which modulation cannot be detected. This is a very large excursion which would be unlikely to be reached in domestic circumstances by reasonably sensitive speakers, although it could be exceeded in high power disco set-ups. At normal listening levels the doppler effect is rather like that of an ambulance travelling at walking-pace. Really then, its effect can be discounted and need not deter anyone wishing to use single full-range speakers instead of multiple units.

The Tweeter

Turning now to the tweeter, we find that it uses the same general principle as the bass speakers, although there are some differences apart from size. One noticeable feature is that unlike the bass speaker the back of the unit is totally enclosed. This is to prevent the tweeter cone being affected by the large air pressure differences that are generated inside the cabinet by the bass speaker.

To achieve a high rigidity-to-density ratio and so avoid buckling and other cone deformations that can be produced by the high accelerations it can encounter, metal such as aluminium and beryllium has been used as a cone material. This increases the sound velocity within the material which pushes the first break-up mode higher up the frequency scale. However, rigidity can also produce a problem in that there is little or no flexure, so the radiation resistance falls off at an earlier point than with a less rigid cone and the treble response suffers accordingly. The use of metal-coned tweeters thus tends to be confined to narrow bandwidths, with super-tweeters covering the highest octave or so. Other than these, paper with a high kapok content and mica are the principal materials.

Another feature with many tweeters is that the conventional cone is reversed to form a dome. This overcomes some of the problems associated with cones and gives a wider angle of dispersion. While high-frequency beaming can be useful to a limited extent to concentrate the high frequencies in front of a full-range speaker and so enhance its treble response, if too pronounced with a tweeter, it results in an unpleasant over-emphasis of treble for those listening on axis, and a deficiency of treble for those not directly in front. A dome tends to disperse high frequencies and reduce beaming.

As mentioned earlier, temperature rise can be a problem as the small size does not lend itself to rapid dissipation of heat. Liquid cooling of the air gap with colloidal ferromagnetic fluid which also helps to concentrate the magnetic flux is employed with some models.

Phasing

Whenever more than one speaker is to be operated in the same air space it is essential that correct phasing be observed. Sound waves consist of alternate compression and rarefied regions of air that spread out at high speed (1,090 ft, 332 m per second at 0°C at sea level) from the source. If there are two loudspeakers working close together, and they are not in phase, the cone of one moves backward while that of the other moves forward.

The compression wave produced by the one will therefore merge with the rarefaction generated by the other, and the two will cancel. Cancellation is greater at wavelengths longer than the distance between the speakers which means that the bass suffers most. With speakers that are very close such as on the same baffle, frequencies right up to the treble range are cancelled. When constructing speakers having multiple drivers, it is therefore very important to ensure that they are wired correctly.

To enable this to be done, one of the speaker terminals is marked with a plus sign or a red spot. All such must be connected to the same terminal of the amplifier. In the case of a stereo pair, they must be connected with similar terminals going to similar contacts on the amplifier output sockets.

If a loudspeaker is to be used with unmarked terminals, they can be identified by one of two methods. One way is to connect it to an amplifier together with another speaker that is marked, and stand them side by side. Play some music with a good bass content, then reverse the connections to one speaker. Connected one way, the music will sound full with plenty of bass, but the other way it will sound thin with the bass lacking.

When the bass is present they are inphase and the terminals can be marked the same as the known speaker. If both speakers are unmarked but they are to be used together, an arbitrary marking can be made of both sets of terminals to ensure that like terminals will be connected to the same side of the amplifer.

The other method does not need another speaker or amplifier, but requires a 6 or 9-volt dry battery. Connect a pair of leads to the battery, and the other end of one lead to one terminal of the speaker. Rest your fingers lightly on the front of the speaker cone near the centre, and momentarily touch the free end of the second lead to the unconnected speaker

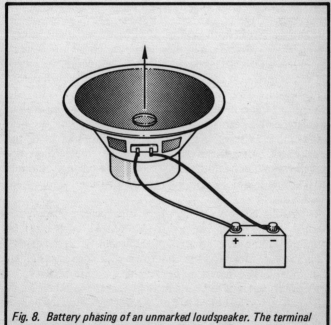

Fig. 8. Battery phasing of an unmarked loudspeaker. The terminal which is connected to the battery positive is the '+' or red spot when the cone moves upward. Contact to battery should be only momentary.

terminal. The cone will be felt to jump slightly either forward or backward. If it jumps forward, the positive pole of the battery is connected to the plus terminal which should thus be marked. If it moves backward toward the magnet, the negative battery pole is connected to the speaker plus terminal (Fig. 8).

If the speaker is not very sensitive or the battery is low, it may be difficult to determine whether the cone moved forward or backward. If in doubt reverse the connections and try again. The difference in direction of movement should be now apparant by comparison. Cables used to connect speakers should always have some means of identifying the conductors so that the speakers can be correctly phased.

Chapter 2

ALTERNATIVE DRIVERS

Although the moving coil driver has reigned supreme as the principal sound reproducer for many decades, it has had several challengers. These have been developed to avoid some of the problems associated with the moving coil unit, but they have had their own drawbacks. These are some of the main ones.

Electrostatic Speakers

The moving member that produces the sound pressure waves in an electrostatic speaker is a thin plastic diaphragm that is coated with a conductive deposit. The basic unit has a rigid metal back plate from which the diaphragm is separated by a thin layer of air. When a high voltage is applied across the diaphragm and plate, there is a mutual electrostatic attraction between them which pulls the diaphragm taut toward the plate.

The attraction is dependant on the voltage applied, so if the voltage is made to vary in sympathy with the signal, the diaphragm moves accordingly and so generates sound pressure waves at its front surface.

One attraction of this system is that the diaphragm is driven over its whole surface by the applied voltage, unlike the moving coil cone which is driven only from its apex. Thus the whole surface moves in unison without any of the buckling or other spurious distortion-producing motions suffered by the cone. This gives rise to another major advantage. As it is wholly under the control of the applied signal, it does not need to be made rigid, which in turn means that it can be extremely light. Having thereby a very small mass, it responds readily to sudden signal changes and so is an excellent reproducer of high frequencies and transients.

The first snag is that both positive and negative half-cycles of an applied signal cause movement of the diaphragm in the same direction, toward the back plate, because attraction is not dependant on polarity. This produces an effect termed *frequency doubling* as the diaphragm moves backwards and forwards twice for each cycle. Fortunately this one is easily overcome. The a.c. signal is superimposed on a fixed d.c. potential which serves as a bias. Thus the signal adds and subtracts from the steady bias voltage on alternate half-cycles, and the diaphragm moves accordingly.

Push-Pull

The electrostatic charge depends not only on the applied voltage but also on the spacing between the two members. The closer they are, the greater the attraction. This poses another problem. As the diaphragm move backwards and forwards the spacing also varies. So the attraction depends on the position of the diaphragm at any instant. The signal has a greater influence when the gap is narrow than when it is wide, which is at the peak of one half-cycle, so the response is non-linear, and amplitude distortion results. Especially is this the case for the lower frequencies at which diaphragm excursion is at its greatest.

Here again there is a neat answer. It is to employ two plates that are acoustically transparant such as a mesh, one on either side of the diaphragm. The signal is split in phase into two of opposite polarity, usually by means of a transformer secondary winding with a centre-tap. These are applied along with the d.c. bias between the diaphragm and each of the rigid plates. So at each half-cycle, the attraction hence the distance between the diaphragm and one plate is increased, while that to the other is diminished. The reduced force on one side is thereby balanced by the increased force on the other. This is known as *push-pull* system, a principle also used in amplifier output stages. Harmonic distortion is thereby cancelled out.

Charge Migration

There is still another problem. The device is really a large capacitor and so behaves as such. Like any capacitor, current flows in when a voltage is applied and charges it up to a limit that depends on the value of the capacitance. If the capacitance varies, current flows in and out in sympathy with the variation. Capacitance depends on the spacing between the elements of any capacitor. So, when the diaphragm moves and the spacing varies, so does the capacitances, and thus also the stored charge, Now attraction between the diaphragm and the fixed plates depends not only on the applied voltage and the spacing, but also on the electrical charge that is stored in it. If this varies, so does the attraction and thereby the diaphragm excursion.

Therefore, the diaphragm motion is not dependant totally on the applied signal, but also the charge flowing in and out of the device, which thereby introduces distortion. Again there is a simple solution. It consists of including a high value series resistor in the bias supply (Fig. 9). The time constant of the resistor/capacitance combination is very long compared to the lowest frequency to be reproduced, it is in fact a matter of

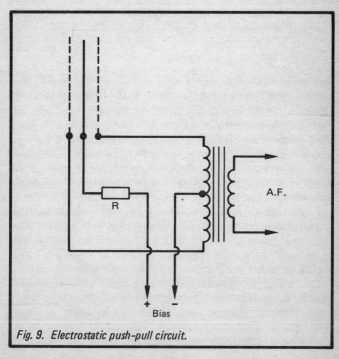

Fig. 9. Electrostatic push-pull circuit.

25

minutes rather than seconds. This permits very little charge to flow in and out during the diaphragm excursions, so the applied force is due soley to the signal voltage.

There is yet a further snag though. If one part of the diaphragm becomes closer to one of the plates than another, the local capacitance of that area increases and the charge present will flow to that point from an adjacent area that is not so close. The attraction at that point thus becomes greater producing a further movement toward the plate.

So the diaphram fails to move equally over its whole area, and any minor differences quickly multiply. The solution to this problem is similar to that of the last one, introduce high resistance to limit the flow of current from one part of the diaphgram to another. This is achieved by making the conductive coating highly resistive, as it does not have to be a good conductor to function. Typically, the coating is given one conductive atom to ten million non-conductive ones and has a measured resistance of hundreds of megohms.

Frequency Response Anomalies

The radiating pattern of the electrostatic speaker is that of a doublet, that is it radiates equally from the front and from the back. It is thus similar to a moving coil speaker on a flat baffle. As a compression wave is generated by one side at the same time as a rarefaction wave is radiated by the other, cancellation occurs when the two meet at the edge. This occurs at all wavelengths longer than the radius of the doublet, so the response at such wavelengths which correspond to the lower frequencies, is poor.

To minimise this the speaker can be made very large, or it can be placed in a cabinet. The latter course is universally used for moving coil drivers, but is impractical for electrostatic units because the high pressures built up in a cabinet would greatly influence the movement of the very light diaphragm.

To produce a reasonable bass response then, the speaker must be large. However, this can have an adverse effect on the treble response. The reason for this is that while all sound produced on-axis is coherent, arriving at the listener at the same time this is not so at any point off-axis. If the difference in distance from one point on the diaphragm to the listener, and another point on the diaphragm to the listener is equal to half a wavelength, cancellation of that frequency will occur. With a large speaker, many such points will occur at different wavelengths across the width of the diaphragm as the listener moves off-axis. The shorter the wavelength the greater the number of points within the width. So, the high frequency response suffers at all off-axis positions.

The early Quad electrostatic speakers minimised this effect by using three units, a narrow centre one to handle the high frequencies, and two bass ones on either side. This required the use of a crossover circuit to separate the treble from the bass and added to the complication of the drive circuitry.

In the later models the conductive coating is divided into five concentric rings with a centre and two outside segments making eight in all. These are fed from a sequential delay line so that the signal is first applied to the centre, and then consecutively at 24 μS delays with attenuation to the other sections. A spherical-fronted wave is thereby produced which simulates a point source situated some 30 cm behind the diaphragm. Such a source has a wide angle of dispersion with no cancellation effects off-axis.

Flash-over

The voltage required for polarising an electrostatic speaker is quite high, (5.25 kV with the Quad), and the signal voltage must be of similar order. As the spacing must be kept small to obtain maximum electrostatic attraction and sensitivity, there is an ever present risk of flash-over which could damage the diaphragm. Reducing the applied voltage is not the answer as this also reduces sensitivity.

One speaker has the entire unit sealed in an inert gas which inhibits flashovers and thereby permits higher voltages and greater power output. Another (the later Quad) senses the ionisation which precedes a flashover by means of an aerial running around the frame. When it is detected a triac 'crowbar' circuit is immediately activated which short circuits the amplifier output with a 1.5 Ω resistor! There is also a limiter circuit which adds audible distortion when the input signal from the amplifier exceeds 40 V.

Another method of flash-over protection is to use thermoplastic coated with a conductive material on the outer surface for the rigid plates instead of metal. Thus the plate material serves as an insulator to inhibit flash-overs, although the extra spacing to the active outer coating inevitably reduces sensitivity.

We have described the electrostatic speaker and its snags at some length, for a purpose. At first glance it may appear that its low-mass diaphragm and the even drive over the entire area virtually solves the problems inherent with the moving-coil unit which it should have ousted years ago. These observations should show that while successful electrostatics have indeed been produced, they are not without drawbacks and complications. The moving-coil unit thus remains the most practical means of sound reproduction.

Orthodynamic Drivers

The orthodynamic speaker uses a thin plastic diaphragm driven over its whole surface in a similar manner to the electrostatic, but the impelling force is electromagnetic. It thus avoids many of the problems associated with the electrostatic, one of the principal ones being the elimination of a polarising voltage and high signal voltages with their risk of flash-over.

The diaphragm has a pattern of copper or aluminium conductors etched on to it in a similar manner to that of a printed circuit. Magnetic fields are set up over the diaphragm surface by either short individual bar magnets mounted on both sides perpendicularly to the surface, or by two plates of ceramic magnetic material on either side. The plates have holes over their whole area to permit the sound pressure waves to be radiated, and they have magnetized zones between the holes. Each zone is equivalent to an individual bar magnet. (Fig.10).

The outer ends of each magnet or magnetic zone are linked with a ferrous plate or surface so that adjacent magnets are in series and thereby form a U magnet with the free poles facing the diaphragm surface. The magnetic field thereby passes from one pole, then longitudinally along the surface, and back to the adjacent opposite pole on the same side.

On the opposite side of the diaphragm, the magnets are arranged so that the poles are of the same polarity as those

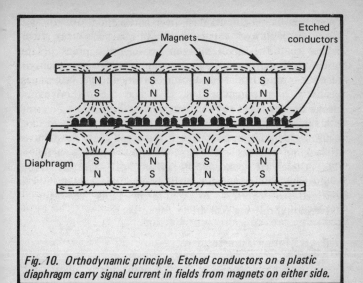

Fig. 10. Orthodynamic principle. Etched conductors on a plastic diaphragm carry signal current in fields from magnets on either side.

facing them on the first side. As like poles and magnetic fields mutually repel, the fields are concentrated at the halfway point between them which is where the diaphragm is. Thus maximum field concentration is obtained at the diaphragm

Conductor Pattern

A simple spiral or zig-zag pattern for the etched conductor cannot be used because current in adjacent runs would be travelling in opposite directions. This would produce magnetic forces impelling adjacent parts of the diaphragm in different directions. So a more complex pattern of loops that double back on themselves must be employed to ensure that all conductors lying within the same magnetic field direction carry signal current in the same direction.

The metal conductors etched onto the diaphragm must carry current and so be of greater thickness than the conductive coating of the electrostatic diaphragm. As a result the mass is greater and so the transient and treble response is not quite that of the electrostatic although it is very good. There must be reasonable air spacing between the magnets and the diaphragm to allow diaphragm excursion, so this is necessarily much greater than the small air gap between the poles of the moving-coil driver. As any air gap in a magnetic circuit introduces magnetic resistance (*reluctance*), the larger gap means greater magnetic losses. Hence the orthodynamic speaker is less sensitive than a moving-coil unit.

A similar problem exists to that of the electrostatic speaker regarding diaphragm size. If it is too small, bass frequencies are lacking, whereas if it is large enough to produce sufficient bass, there are cancellation effects off axis at treble frequencies. Because of this, orthodynamic speakers have been confined to tweeters or mid-range units requiring a conventional moving-coil driver for the bass.

Heil Air Motion Transformer

This device is a variation on the orthodynamic driver having an etched conductor on a plastic diaphragm that operates within applied magnetic fields, but has two main differences. The first is that the magnetic fields are at right angles to the diaphragm instead of being in the same plane.

The second is in the nature and motion of the diaphragm itself. It is not flat but is arranged in folds like a concertina. Instead of producing a backwards and forwards motion, the direction of the magnetic field imparts a sideways movement. This causes the folds in the diaphragm to open and close, sucking air in and squeezing it out (Fig. 11).

Most other drivers employ a lot of energy to move a small amount of air with the result that the efficiency is low; a large amount of electrical watts is required to produce a small number of acoustic watts. Rather like driving a car along a flat road in bottom gear. The idea of the air motion transformer is to change up to a higher gear. A small movement of the diaphragm produces a much larger air motion. It is similar to the squeezing of an orange pip between the fingers, small finger movement and pressure can send the pip yards.

Here again, the problems of combining good high and low frequency response has limited the device to tweeters and mid-range units. The higher acoustic efficiency is partly offset

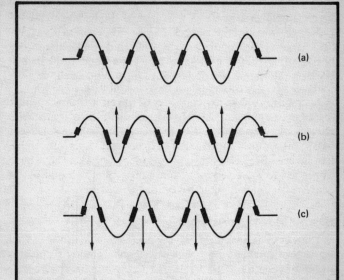

Fig. 11. Heil Air Motion Transformer. The diaphragm is formed into concertina folds (a). Alternate attraction and repulsion of conductors on adjacent folds squeeze air alternately from each side, (b & c). Large volumes of air are moved by small diaphragm motion.

by the lower magnetic efficiency which is inherent with the orthodynamic principle. In any case, efficiency has to be matched to that of the bass unit to achieve a tonal balance, so high efficiency in a tweeter or mid-range unit is not of itself important. Smooth response and low distortion are more so.

Ribbon Tweeter

The principle of this unit is the same as a ribbon microphone in reverse. The ribbon is formed of aluminium foil which is corrugated or ribbed to allow forward and backward motion when it is suspended from its ends between powerful magnet pole pieces. It is mounted edgeways to these so that its movements it at right angles to them, and the air gap between ribbon edge and pole piece is very small

The signal current is passed along the ribbon which sets up a magnetic field that interacts with that of the magnets and so produces a force on the ribbon. The electrodynamic principle is the same as that of the moving coil, and in fact it can be considered as a moving coil speaker with a single turn. Being very light the ribbon responds well to high frequencies, and as it is impelled over its whole area it is free from the distortions inherent with a cone reproducer. (Fig. 12).

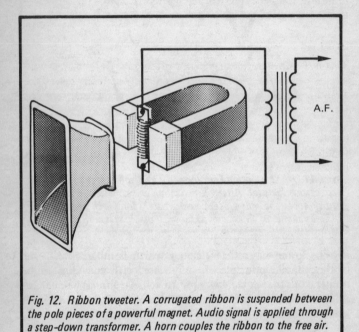

Fig. 12. Ribbon tweeter. A corrugated ribbon is suspended between the pole pieces of a powerful magnet. Audio signal is applied through a step-down transformer. A horn couples the ribbon to the free air.

Its small area precludes its use for bass or even mid-frequencies. A wider ribbon would increase the gap between the magnetic pole pieces and so weaken the field resulting in low efficiency; so there is a limit to its size. Even at high frequencies it efficiency is not great so it usually has a horn mounted in front to provide a more effective air coupling.

The horn also restricts the lower frequency range as its size governs the lowest frequency at which it is effective, and there is a practical limit to its size. Coloration occurs at the frequency where horn efficiency falls off, so the tweeter is usually operated well above that point in conjunction with a crossover network and bass and mid-range speakers.

The impedance of the ribbon is very low, just a fraction of an ohm, so coupling to the amplifier output must be via a matching transformer. This must be carefully designed to minimise frequency and other forms of distortion otherwise the advantage of the ribbon's low distortion would be lost.

Plasma Tweeter

This is a rather exotic device not often encountered, but with interesting features. 'The moving part' which generates the sound is the lightest one of all, an electric arc! When an arc is set up between a pair of electrical conductors local heat of high temperature is generated which causes a violent expansion of the air in the immediate vicinity. Sound is thereby produced, a familiar example being the clap of thunder resulting from a lightning stroke.

If the arc is modulated with an audio signal its intensity varies accordingly and so does the heat produced. Air expansion likewise varies and thereby also the sound pressure wave. So sound is generated in sympathy with the modulation.

A number of tweeters have been produced over a period of many years using this or a similar principle. One recent one consists of a sphere of a fine mesh having at its centre a fine needle electrode. A high radio-frequency electrical potential at 27 MHz which is derived from a crystal oscillator, is applied between the needle and the sphere. Positive and negative ions are produced alternately, and the air in the vicinity of this corona discharge is heated to a temperature of 1,500°C.

The audio signal is amplitude modulated on the r.f., and so the intensity of the corona changes, also varying the heat around the 1,500°C mean. A spherical sound wave which is totally in phase, is thus radiated around the device at all angles. There are thus no frequency response differences at any off-axis position.

As it is the air itself that initiates the sound wave, there are no low-efficiency coupling problems, furthermore there are no resonance or coloration effects caused by physical moving parts. The frequency response extends from 4.5 - 150 kHz, which is considerably beyound the audio range. Total harmonic distortion is less than 1% at any part of its frequency range, and the maximum output is 95 dB at 1 metre.

That high temperature may sound dangerous, but actually it is not. The *amount* of heat is quite small and it is not even sufficient to heat the sphere to any noticeable extent. Temperature is not a measure of the amount of heat. A teaspoonful of boiling water contains less heat than a bucketful at hand temperature.

A filter is included with the unit so that it can be connected directly across existing speakers to extend the treble response. Its range is excessive, but the all round in-phase feature as well as the low coloration is very attractive. If a full range version that would produce bass frequencies could be devised, this could be the ultimate loudspeaker. Its main drawback at present is the price.

Piezo Tweeter

Coming now to a more practical propostion, especially for the home constructor, we now consider the piezo tweeter. There are a number of substances that change dimensions if they are subject to an applied voltage, or generate a potential if subject to mechanical stress. A naturally occurring one is Rochelle salt which was once used for audio devices such as microphones and gramophone pickups. It is fragile though, and its performance is subject to humidity changes. Now, manufactured ceramic materials such as lead zirconate titinate have replaced it, as these are more stable and robust.

The simplest device is termed a *monomorph* which consists of a single slice of the ceramic, but the movement produced by the voltage-induced dimensional change is very small.

An improvement is to cement two slices together to form a *bimorph*. The combination is secured at one end and a voltage is applied in such a manner that one slice shrinks while the other lengthens. This produces a bending action with a sideways displacement of the free end. Movement is thus much greater than with a single slice. The bimorph is of itself too small to produce much sound as the movement is less than most other types of tweeter. It is therefore linked to a cone or coupled to the air via a horn like the ribbon tweeter.

The device is capacitive which means that there is no direct resistance across it and the impedance consists mostly of capacitive reactance. The practical effect of this is that the impedance is very high at low frequencies dropping to around 1,000 Ω at 1 kHz, from which is falls smoothly to 30 Ω at 40 kHz. A consequence of this is that it can be connected directly across a bass speaker without the need of a crossover network. This is a major advantage as the crossover circuit is the source of many evils as we shall see in a later chapter.

Having no coil appended to its apex like the moving coil tweeter, the cone has a much lower mass. It therefore has a superior transient response and a frequency range up to 40 kHz. Its response is smooth, typically within ± 2 dB from 3 — 30 kHz. Distortion is around 0.5% over most of its range rising to just over 1% at 1 kHz. The unit will accept continuous signals of 15 volts, which is 28 watts into 8 Ω or intermittent music peaks of 30 volts, which is 110 watts into 8 Ω. It thus has ample power handling capacity. One maker who has a range of piezo tweeters is Motorola, and these are probably the best choice of tweeter for the home constructor.

Chapter 3

BOXING CLEVER

When the cone of a moving coil speaker moves backwards and forwards it generates two separate sound waves, one at the front and the other at the back. Air is compressed in one direction while that in the other is rarefied. The two waves are thus said to be out of phase.

Phase is often described by comparing it with an imaginary line rotating round a central point, a device termed a vector. At a half-revolution which is 180°, the signals are displaced by one half-cycle, and are totally out of phase. At 90°, the signals are a quarter-cycle displaced and are said to be in *quadrature*. Two out-of-phase signals can be represented by two lines drawn one from the end of the other at the appropriate angle, and if they are drawn to scale with the length representing signal amplitude, the value of the resulting signal (the *resultant*) can be found. This is done by simply joining the end of the second to the start of the first by a third line to form a triangle. The length of the third line then gives the amplitude of the resultant (Fig. 13).

It is useful to be familiar with these concepts as they frequently appear in technical discussions where out-of-phase signals are involved, such as with loudspeaker systems.

Such a case is a loudspeaker generating two 180° out-of-phase signals at its front and rear. When these meet at the rim of the speaker, the compression regions merge and fill the rarefaction zones so little sound is actually radiated. Of that which is, only high frequencies having a wavelength shorter than the radius of the cone remain, as one or more complete cycles of these are propagated before cancellation occurs at the rim. This accounts for the familiar tinny effect when a loudspeaker is operated without a baffle.

It is evident then that some means must be provided to keep the two out of phase waves physically apart; this is the sole purpose of the speaker cabinet or enclosure as it is now more usually called. As we shall see there is a lot more involved in this than at first may appear. Much ingenuity has gone into the

36

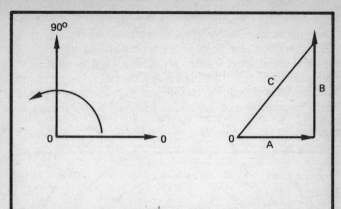

Fig. 13. Vectors. Signal amplitudes are indicated by line lengths and phase by angles. During a complete cycle, line rotates through 360°. If two signals A and B are drawn one from the end of the other, the phase angle and amplitude of the resultant is determined by a joining line C.

design of these boxes, —boxing clever in fact. But every known method has disadvantages so it is a case of choosing which set of disadvantages are least objectionable. We will explore the various methods in common use, size up their good and bad points, then we can make an informed choice or perhaps even design our own.

In passing it may be noted that the ideal reproducer would be a pulsating sphere rather than a backward-and-forward moving cone. This would radiate in-phase sound in all directions and so eliminate all the problems associated with the disposal of the rear wave. Many attempts have been made to achieve such a device but none so far successful. The nearest has been the plasma speaker described in the last chapter, but this covers only the high frequencies whereas it is the bass that presents the problems.

Baffle/Doublet

An obvious way to keep the waves apart is to mount the speaker on a large flat board which is termed a baffle. They still meet at the edge, but they have further to go and so longer wavelengths can be propagated before cancellation takes place. Thus the bass response is extended compared to that of an unmounted speaker (Fig. 14). The straightforward baffle has many advantages, among which is the lack of air resonance that produces the coloration inherent with an enclosure. Also panel resonances and vibrations common with cabinets are minimal.

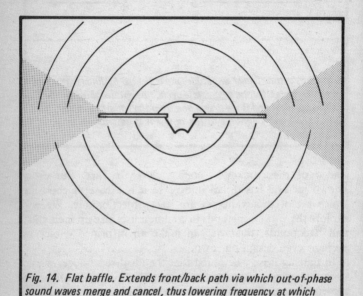

Fig. 14. Flat baffle. Extends front/back path via which out-of-phase sound waves merge and cancel, thus lowering frequency at which cancellation occurs.

One potential snag is that because of the time taken for the rear sound waves to reach the edge of the baffle, delays occur which at some frequencies can mean that a compression wave from the rear is propagated at the same time as the next compression wave from the front, so that they actually reinforce each other. At other frequencies the opposite occurs and cancellation takes place. Reinforcement occurs at wavelengths that are 0.5, 1.5, 2.5 ... times the radius of the baffle, whereas cancellation takes place at whole multiples, 1.0, 2.0, 3.0 ... times the radius.

The net effect of this is a very uneven frequency response with alternate peaks and troughs throughout its range. It can be easily avoided by simply mounting the speaker off centre on the baffle. There is thus no uniform radius and the cancellation and reinforcementeffects are smoothed out. A rectangular baffle with the speaker off centre gives good results, but a circular or square one with the speaker at the centre is the worst possible case (Fig. 15).

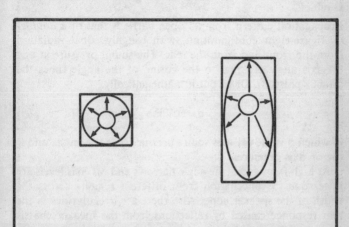

Fig. 15. A speaker in the centre of a square baffle has an almost equal radius to the baffle edge so cancellation occurs at whole multiples of the radius wavelength and reinforcement at half multiples. This effect is avoided in a rectangular baffle where the radius is not the same in all directions thus smoothing out interference effects.

The big problem with an open baffle lies in the size of baffle needed to procure an adequate bass response. To achieve a flat response down to 45 Hz, requires a baffle with the shortest radius of 25 ft (7.7 m). That means a width and height of more than 50 ft, which is obviously impossible for domestic use, and most other uses too!

Looking at more practical dimensions, a 2ft radius which is a 4 ft width or height would be about the maximum, especially

39

as two are needed for stereo. This would start to roll off at 280 Hz which is inadequate for hi-fi, but an ameliorating factor is that the bass fall-off is only 6 dB per octave. This means a − 6dB response at 140 Hz, and a − 12 dB level at 70 Hz. The bass response of most enclosures drop sharply below their rated limit, so with a baffle of this size there is at least some response in the bass though not very much. A further factor is that the reproduction sounds more natural and musical when the fall-off is gradual than when it is abrupt.

Doublet

Propagation pattern from an open baffle is that of a *doublet* or figure-eight configuration, with roughly equal radiation from the front and from the rear. The sound pressure at any off-axis angle is equal to the cosine of the angle times the on-axis pressure. Or to put it mathematically:

$$p = \cos\theta P$$

in which p is the off-axis sound pressure, θ is the angle, and P the on-axis pressure.

At high frequencies the angle narrows and off-axis levels are lower due to cancellation from different regions across the width of the speaker cone. Also there are irregularities in the rear responce caused by reflections from the speaker chassis and magnet assembly.

Because of the strong rear propagation, an open baffle should be operated well clear of a backing wall otherwise reflections from it will reinforce and cancel quarter and half wavelengths and their multiples, of the spacing between the baffle and the wall. Modification of the doublet radiation pattern can be obtained by mounting two baffle speakers in a V configuration.

Adding Sides

The dimensions of a baffle can be increased by adding sides, a top and a bottom. If these are narrow compared to the total width of the baffle there will be little adverse effect and the front-to-back path is extended thereby slightly improving the bass response. Increasing the width of the sides further extends the bass, but at the expense of a degree of coloration due to resonance of the air in the structure which behaves as a short pipe. However, as the width of the 'pipe' is large compared to its length, the effect is not great.

A further step is to add a back in which a number of slots have been cut. This adds to the front-to-back path and the slots serve as an acoustic resistance to the rear wave. So the bass is noticeably increased. However, the enclosed space has a more pronounced resonance which affects the reproduction. The back itself could resonate, being of a large unbraced area, unless it was of substantial thickness and screwed at frequent intervals around its perimeter.

Really, we now have a conventional loudspeaker cabinet such as used for medium quality audio systems. The bass is still deficient compared to that of a well-designed enclosure, but the reproduction is likely to be less coloured and more natural than many so-called hi-fi units.

Such a cabinet can give very satisfactory results if robustly constructed and made large enough to give a reasonable bass response. Dimensions are not critical but it is best to make the front as large as practicable, and the sides not too deep. The speaker should be off centre, but it need not be off centre relative to the width, the condition is satisfied if it is mounted toward the top half of the cabinet. If it is too far off centre the shortest path from front-to-back is reduced and with it the bass response.

A practical shape to take account of the above condition is to make the cabinet much taller than it is wide. Most listening rooms have floor space limitations but no reasonable limit as to height. The short path from the speaker unit to the top edge can then be made larger than the paths from the speaker to the sides. It should not be equal to them. Bass response is then dependant on the width.

An interesting possibility for extending the width of either a flat baffle or a cabinet is the use of folding doors. A pair of doors are hinged at the sides of the baffle or cabinet, so that they either close in front or are pushed back against the sides. When open, they form wings or extensions to increase the width, but are closed when not in use to save space (Fig. 16).

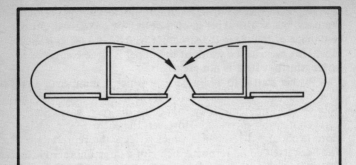

Fig. 16. Extending doors can increase the front-to-back with an open-backed cabinet of modest width.

As each door can be half the width of the baffle, the two effectively double its width. There may be insufficient room to accommodate such a width even temporarily during listening sessions in which case the doors can be made narrower. They would then look rather odd when closed over the front as they wouldn't meet, so it might be better to have narrow doors folding back. The hinges should be full length piano hinges to eliminate air gaps between door and baffle, and if possible some means of locking the doors firmly open is desirable.

Coloration, though comparatively small could be reduced further by making the cabinet an irregular shape if one's woodworking skills are up to it. An irregular pentagon or hexagon are possibilities, or perhaps more simply a quadrangle with non-parallel sides. Ideally the speaker should be mounted in the widest portion to maintain a long minimum front-to-back path. If this is at the top though, care would be needed to ensure stability.

Whatever mode of construction is considered, size will always be the main obstacle to obtaining good results from a baffle or simple cabinet. This is compounded by the strong rear wave which means that the speakers must be placed well away from any wall and thus take up even more room. For this reason, and especially in view of limited space in modern living accommodation, coupled with the desire for high quality sound reproduction, other means are employed to dispose of the rear wave. These generally offer a good bass response with moderate size, but as may be expected, there are penalties.

Infinite Baffle

An obvious and seemingly simple way of keeping the front and the rear wave apart is to mount the speaker in a sealed air-tight box so that the rear wave is totally confined to it. It is the method most commonly used for hi-fi speakers as it achieves an extended bass response with moderate and in some cases quite small size.

As the baffle has no edges around which the two waves can merge it has been dubbed *infinite baffle*, but as the size of the box is by no means infinite it is really a mismomer. The bass driver used for this type of enclosure requires a weaker or more compliant suspension than other types because the springiness of the trapped air restrains the cone movement and therefore itself serves as a suspension. The driver and the enclosure is therefore often described as of the *acoustic suspension* type.

An important restriction must be observed with these drivers. They should never be used in ordinary unsealed cabinets. Without the cushion of air behind the cone, the mechanical suspension is too weak to hold it in place by itself, and damage would soon result.

The big snag with this principle is that the air cushion can considerably modify the motion of the cone, and so distort the front sound wave radiated from it. We saw in the first chapter that the resonant frequency of a bass driver should be as low as possible, because the response falls off rapidly at the rate of 12 dB per octave below it.

The dampening effect of the trapped air on the cone decreases compliance and results in a raising of its resonant frequency. The larger the box, the greater the volume of air it encloses, the larger its compliance and the smaller its dampening effect. This is so because a given cone excursion exercises less compression on a large air volume than on a small volume. Hence our first rule for infinite baffle enclosures is: *with a given driver a large box has a lower resonant frequency than a small one.*

43

Using the same logic, a small cone compresses a given air volume less than a large cone. So the cone size also influences the enclosure resonant frequency, so our second rule is: *a small cone produces a lower enclosure resonant frequency than a large one*. However, because of its smaller mass it had a higher free-air resonance to start with.

Putting all this together, three things affect the resonant frequency of the enclosure, 1) air volume, hence box size; 2) cone size; and 3) cone mass. As we saw in chapter 1, the compliance of the cone surround also affects the resonant frequency, but with this type of driver the surround compliance is a minor factor compared to that of the air in the box.

A desired resonant frequency can thus be obtained by selection of these three factors. If one or two are immutable, then the required result can be achieved by selecting the other. The accompanying chart shows the relationships and enables a selection to be made (Fig. 17).

Damping and Q

At the enclosure resonant frequency, the cone excursion is larger than at all other frequencies, hence the sound output is greater, and a peak appears in the frequency response. If undamped, this results in a boomy sounding bass, one note predominates, in fact the effect has been dubbed 'one-note bass'

The magnification of cone movement at resonance compared to that at other frequencies is denoted by the letter Q. Students of electronics will recognise that this is the term applied to an inductor to denote its reactance divided by its resistance. A high Q means the coil will tune sharply with a large peak and so it is rated as a quality factor, hence the designation.

In the case of a loudspeaker, the same term is used to describe a like magnification at a resonant frequency, but here Q is rather a mismnomer as the result is the opposite of quality.

When a loudspeaker cone is impelled backwards and forwards by the applied electrical signal, the coil windings are

44

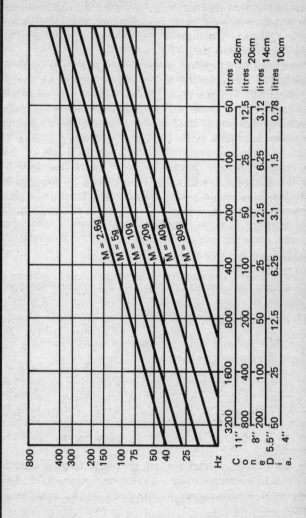

Fig. 17. Resonant frequency from enclosure volume, cone diameter and cone mass.

45

cutting through the magnetic field and so a voltage is generated in them. This voltage is of opposite polarity to the applied voltage, hence it is termed *back emf*. This voltage produces a back current which flows through the coil and through the output circuits of the amplifier. Although the output impedance of most amplifiers are rated at around $4-8$ Ω, this is a nominal figure to which the total loudspeaker impedance should be matched for efficient and safe operation. The actual resistance offered to a current flowing in the output circuits is very much lower, a fraction of an ohm in most cases.

Compared to the resistance of the coil, the amplifier output resistance is negligible, so the back current is limited mainly by the coil resistance. The current sets up a magnetic field around the coil which exerts a force that opposes the original motion. Now this opposing force is not proportional to the applied signal, but to the original cone motion which generated it. So, an excessive cone motion at any one frequency produces a larger opposing force at that frequency. It can be seen from this then, that the opposing force is greater at any peak resulting from a resonance, and thereby the Q is reduced and the peak is dampened.

The degree of dampening depends on the magnitude of the opposing force, which in turn depends on the efficiency of the system as a generator. Generator efficiency is governed by the magnetic flux density and the length of the coil, and inversely by the coil resistance, the cone inertia which depends on its mass, and the frequency of resonance.

There are thus mechanical factors and electrical ones that make up the total Q of the system. These are designated as Q_{ms} and Q_{es} in maker's specifications. They are combined in the following formula to describe the total Q of a driver, Q_{ts}:

$$Q_{ts} = \frac{Q_{ms} \times Q_{es}}{Q_{ms} + Q_{es}} \quad \text{or} \quad \frac{1}{Q_{ts}} = \frac{1}{Q_{ms}} + \frac{1}{Q_{es}}$$

The total Q designated Q_{ts}, is that of the driver only. The total including the cabinet is described as Q_{tc}. This of course cannot be specified by a manufacturer because he does not know the size of the cabinet in which the driver will be used,

46

but it does appear in formula which we can use to determine the optimum cabinet size as we shall see.

If Q_{tc} is equal to unity, there is no peak at the resonant frequency because the amplitude of the cone excursion is just 1 times that at any other frequency. This would appear to be the ideal value. However, an undamped response consists of a peak that is sharp at its tip while being fairly broad at its base. If now we level the tip to unity value, there is still a slight rise on either side due to the 'foothills' of the base. The lower one disappears due to the bass roll off below resonance, but the upper one remains.

A Q_{tc} of unity therefore produces a small rise just above the resonant frequency. The chart shows the effect (Fig. 18). To eliminate this, we need a Q_{tc} that is actually less than unity. This is possible by reducing the cone diameter, or for a given driver, increasing the volume of air in the enclosure, which means increasing its size.

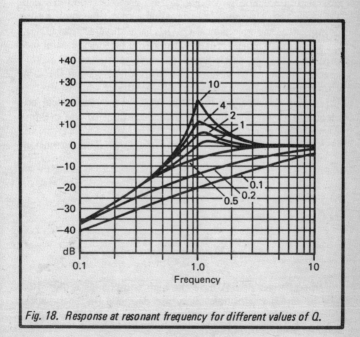

Fig. 18. Response at resonant frequency for different values of Q.

The optimum value to obtain a smooth response is 0.7. although this causes a bass roll off slightly higher than the resonant frequency. If the resonant frequency can be made low by having a large enclosure, the small sacrifice in bass is worth it in order to get a smooth and more natural response. With small enclosures a Q of unity may be necessary to extend the bass as far as possible which means to the resonant frequency. The slight rise just above it further emphasizes the bass and gives the impression of a good bass response, although it is at the expense of naturalness and will give a somewhat boomy result.

Enclosure Size

The formula for designing a sealed enclosure for a particular driver, is quite a complex one, but it can be greatly simplified if its use is restricted to a Q_{tc} of 0.7. For other values it is less accurate. The governing factors are: the compliance of the drive unit's suspension; the volume of air having the same compliance; the mechanical Q, Q_{ms}; and the electrical Q, Q_{es}.

To simplify matters further, these four factors are combined into two in the Thiele-Small parameters quoted in maker's specifications. The volume of a body of air having the same compliance as the suspension of the driver unit is given in litres and denoted by the term V_{as}. The mechanical and electrical Q are usually combined according to the previous formula and given as Q_{ts}.

So we need only the V_{as} and the Q_{ts}. The formula is:

$$V_b = \frac{V_{as} \times Q_{ts}^2}{Q_{tc}^2 - Q_{ts}^2}$$

as Q_{tc} is 0.7, then

$$V_b = \frac{V_{as} \times Q_{ts}^2}{0.49 - Q_{ts}^2}$$

Not all bass drivers have the high compliance required for use in sealed enclosures, many are designed for open-backed systems. If this formula is used for those, it will produce a cabinet volume of impractical size.

48

The volume is of course of air, so it is the internal dimensions that we must use for calculation, and any internal solids must be deducted. The principal one would be the bass driver itself. The volume of this can be approximately calculated by regarding it as a cone. To find the volume of a cone we multiply the area of the base (the speaker cone) by the height (distance from the front of the unit to the back of the magnet) and divide the result by three. Area of the base is given by πr^2. To express all this as a formula we have:

$$V = \frac{\pi r^2 h}{3}$$

In which V is the volume, r is the radius of the speaker, and h is the height.

The tweeter should be calculated the same way. Structural bracing and cross-over units should be allowed for, as should also dense absorbents such as bitumous pads. These items are of greater importance in small enclosures in which they take up a larger proportion of the air space than in larger ones.

Loose absorbent such as BAF wadding actually increases the apparant enclosure volume for a reason we shall explore in a later chapter. Sufficient here to say that the internal air volume can be reduced by about 5% when wadding is used to fill the enclosure.

Sensitivity

The amount of acoustic output from a given electric input is what is meant by the term sensitivity, not the way the speaker responds to transient or other types of signal unless that is specifically stated. For the infinite baffle speaker the sensitivity is low. The reason is not hard to understand. In order achieve a low resonant frequency and thereby obtain an extended bass response without a very large enclosure, the mass of the bass driver is made large. Mass requires power to move it, so more power is needed to do so than for a driver with a lighter cone.

Efficiency, hence sensitivity could be increased by making the magnet stronger, but as we have seen from the Q formula, this reduces the Q and results in overdamping. In turn, overdamping eliminates the effect of resonance on the bass response and results in the bass roll-off starting at a much higher frequency.

The rather unexpected result is that many small speakers need a higher amplifier power to obtain sufficient sound output than larger ones, simply because they are made less efficient in order to get a better bass response.

Dimensional Resonances

In addition to the main air/cone resonance we have discussed, there are air resonances that are functions of the three enclosure dimensions. These resonances occur when the dimension is equal to half a wavelength, and if undamped will cause coloration of the reproduced sound at the corresponding frequencies.

The first thing to ensure is that none of the dimensions are the same. Height width and depth must all be different. This applies also to multiples of those dimensions so that one should not be a half, third or a quarter the size of another. To avoid similar problems in listening rooms, what is known as the *golden ratio* is often invoked. This is to make the dimensions of the room comply with the ratio 1 : 1.6 : 2.5. Any of these can be multiples or sub-multiples such as 1 : 3.2 : 2.5.

The same rule can be applied to infinite baffle enclosures in order to spread the resonances and avoid any coinciding. Should this happen, there would be a very pronounced peak at the frequency corresponding to the half-wavelength. Even worse would be a square box or a rectangle having the same width and depth with the height double the width. That would cause a very strong resonance and severe coloration.

As with the unsealed cabinet, an irregular shape with non-parallel sides reduces dimensional resonance effects. The ultimate shape for doing this is a pyramid, and at least one commercial speaker has been made in this form. The disadvantage apart from the woodworking problems, is that a pyramid has only a third of the volume of a rectangle of the same base area and height. So, either the base and/or height must be increased to compensate, or the reduced bass response inherent with a smaller enclosure must be accepted. As speakers are expected to be compact and have a good bass response, it can be appreciated why the pyramid has not caught on commercially.

When a resonance is excited between two parallel surfaces such as the sides, top and bottom or front and back of an enclosure, what are called *standing waves* are set up. As the half cycles of the waves travelling back and forth are exactly the same length as the space between the surfaces, the respective areas of high and low compression always appear in the same place and so the wave seems to be standing still. The points of minimum vibration are termed the *nodes*, while those of maximum motion are called the *antinodes*.

At the fundamental resonance frequency the antinodes appear halfway between the surfaces, which is at the middle of the enclosure. However, each frequency is accompanied by a number of harmonics, that is further frequencies at double, treble, four times etc, the frequency of the fundamental. These also have a pattern of nodes and antinodes.

The second harmonic has antinodes at one-third and two-thirds of the dimension; the third harmonic antinodes are at one-sixth, a half, and five-sixths the length. Antinodes of the fourth harmonic appear at one-eighth, three-eighths, five-eighths and seven-eighths, and so on.

Dimensional resonances can be dampened by the placing of absorbent material at the antinode positions where the vibrational motion is greatest. It has virtually no effect at the nodes. From the above it is evident that the nodes of the fundamental and all the harmonics are at the surfaces themselves, so material fixed to the cabinet walls have no effect on these resonances. As there are many antinodes of the fundamental and the harmonics spaced across the dimension, and there are further ones from the other two dimensions in the same space, it follows that to be effective, damping material should fill the whole enclosure.

This is done in most of the small enclosures with thick rolled-up layers occupying most of the space. The material used is of a cellular form, so air is present throughout, but the passage of sound pressure waves is impeded. The presence of this material also slightly increases the effective volume of the enclosure because of its slowing down effect on the sound waves passing through it. They thus take longer to reach the boundary wall just as if the dimension was longer and the wall was further away.

With large enclosures there are practical difficulties in completely filling the volume with absorbent. The problem is that the weight causes the material to compact at the bottom and leave gaps at the top. It should not be compressed too much as this forces out the air and so effectively reduces the internal air volume of the enclosure. One solution to this is to fix several 'shelves' of nylon netting (not wire which could vibrate) across the cabinet to support the layers of absorbent.

Panel Resonance

There is yet a further type of resonance which can colour the reproduction from a sealed box type of speaker. The fact that the box *is* sealed and no air can escape produces large pressure differences between the inside surfaces and the external ones which are at the normal atmospheric pressure.

These differences cause the walls of the enclosure to vibrate in and out in sympathy with the pressure differences. They thus produce sound, but because they also have particular resonant frequencies and their motion is not in linear proportion to the pressure, the sound they radiate is highly coloured.

So it is necessary to reduce panel vibrations to the minimum and many different materials and types of construction have been tried with this end in view. One of the best is brick or concrete which has a high density and so a high resistance to lateral vibration. The practical problems are fairly obvious, although with the popular mode of decor for raw brick interior walls and fireplaces, a pair of brick speaker enclosures could match the rest and so not be aesthetically displeasing. With any such projects, the ability of the floor joists to support the result must prudently be considered.

A very effective alternative is sand-filled panels. Each panel is constructed of two sheets of wood separated by square-section moulding around three edges, then sand is poured into the space between them. The fourth edge is finally sealed with a length of moulding. The panels must be made to the correct size as they obviously cannot be cut afterward (Fig. 19).

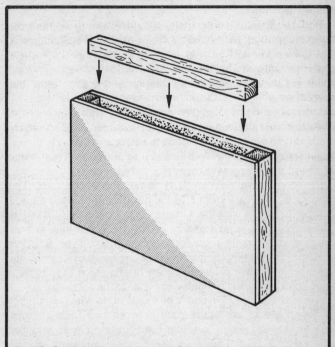

Fig. 19. Sand-filled panel. Two wooden sheets are assembled with square-section along three sides. The cavity is filled with sand and the fourth square-section fitted. Seal all joints to prevent sand leakage.

Perhaps the most common material used is $\frac{3}{8}$ or $\frac{1}{2}$ inch plywood, but it is very prone to vibrate by itself without bracing or damping. To improve matters, many designs employ crossbracing to improve rigidity. While it does this to a certain extent it is not all that effective in reducing vibrations.

The trick is to fit the bracing at the points where the maximum amplitude of vibration occurs, the antinodes. One way of doing this experimentally requires the use of an audio oscillator. The cabinet with drivers in place is temporarily sealed with its back and laid so that the panel under test is uppermost. An amplifier is connected and the oscillator output applied to its input.

Powdered chalk is scattered evenly over the panel, and the amplifier turned well up. The frequency of the oscillator is varied over the low to mid frequency range until the chalk settles in a discernable pattern. The regions where there is no chalk are those of maximum vibration and are the ones that need bracing.

Struts and battens reinforce one point only whereas the vibration nearly always occurs over a larger area. A better method is to use a partition along the affected region. It should have plenty of large holes drilled in it to allow the free passage of sound pressure waves through.

Plywood is available in many thicknesses and grades. The number of plys vary from 3 to 19, but they are always an odd number to inhibit warping. Grades range from type A, which is guaranteed free from surfaces defects to WG which is very rough and normally used for packing cases. Type B/BB is preferred for speaker cabinets because one side is first grade, but the other may have plugs. These are inserts glued in to replace knot holes. This side of course goes inside the enclosure.

Another form of plywood is blockboard, in which a number of rough blocks are sandwiched between two facing sheets, and laminboard which is similar but contains a larger number of smaller blocks. The latter has better damping properties than conventional plywood, but the edges have to be disguised with veneer unless all outside joints are mitred.

Chipboard is another much favoured material. It is made by compressing resin coated wooden chips between steel plates. Here too there are numerous grades. Single layer chipboard consists of chips of the same size throughout and so has a consistent density. Three-layer chipboard has two outer layers of high density to give a better surface finish with a lower density interior. The multi-layer grade has two outer high density layers and also a high density core with lower density in between. There is also a graded density chipboard in which the density varies gradually throughout its thickness (Fig. 20).

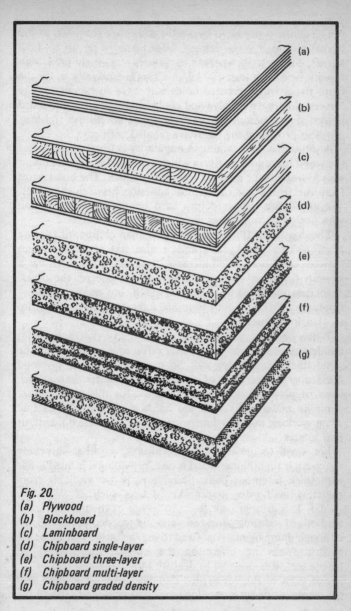

Fig. 20.
(a) Plywood
(b) Blockboard
(c) Laminboard
(d) Chipboard single-layer
(e) Chipboard three-layer
(f) Chipboard multi-layer
(g) Chipboard graded density

The densities are rated by weight and range from 400 to 900 kg/m³ although some cement loaded grades go up to 1150 kg/m³. The best for speaker enclosures is a single layer high density type of at least 600 kg/m³. This is especially so for the front panel where rebated holes may have to be cut for the drivers. Alternatively plywood could be used here. Chipboard is available veneered on one side which solves the finishing problem providing the edges are rebated with care.

Another material gaining in popularity is fibreboard. In this the wood is reduced to fibres which are felted and pressed into sheets with little or no extra resin being added. The bond arises from the felting and the natural adhesion between the fibres. The sheets are tempered into hard boards by impregnation with hot oil or sometimes resin and then heat-cured.

The density of fibreboard is higher than chipboard ranging from 800 to 200 kg/m³, and it also has frictional losses between the fibres which increase its damping factor. It has a smooth finish on one side, and a grainy one on the other. Thickness is limited at present to ½inch, but medium density fibreboard (MDF) from 640 to 860 kg/m³ is now available up to 1½inch thicknesses.

When plywood is used is has been found that lining with builders plaster board has a better effect and is superior to the same thickness of plywood. So a ⅜inch, sheet of plywood bonded to a ⅜inch sheet of plaster board is better than a ¾inch sheet of plywood. Remember to allow for this or any other damping material fixed to the inside surface of the cabinet when working out the dimensions. It is the inside dimensions that matter.

For small to medium sized enclosures, a rather surprising discovery is that thinner wood is best, providing it is lined inside with thick bitumous pads. Suitable pads are available from specialist mail-order loudspeaker dealers such as Wilmslow Audio. This arrangement seems to be one of the most effective methods of reducing panel resonances in wooden enclosures. So although damping material fixed to the the inside surface of the enclosure has no effect on the internal dimensional air resonances, it is essential to deal with the panel resonances.

For most of the panels, the damping need not extend over the whole inside surface as long as it covers at least 60% of the central area. It may be easier for calculating the internal air volume though if it does in fact extend to the edges. The back panel should be fully covered for the following reason.

Reflected Wave

While the rear pressure wave generated by the back of the speaker cone fills the whole enclosure and affects all parts of it, its principal impact is against the rear wall of the enclosure where it is reinforced by direct air particle velocity. A strong wave is therefore reflected back to the loudspeaker. Now paper is transparant to sound waves of mid and lower frequencies as can be proved by taping a sheet of paper over the front of a loudspeaker, the sound is heard at almost undiminished volume. So, when the reflected wave reaches the paper cone of the loudspeaker, it passes straight through it to emerge at the front (Fig. 21).

However, it is delayed compared to the original, by the amount of time it took to travel to and from the rear enclosure wall. When the depth of the enclosure is equal to a quarter or three-quarters of a wavelength, the reflected wave reinforces the original, but when the dimension is a half or a whole wavelength or a multiple, the wave cancels it. Thus we get a series of peaks and troughs in the frequency response corresponding to those frequencies that are reinforced and cancelled.

Sometimes an audible 'honk' is produced by the interaction of the reflected wave with the next cone excursion. To reduce the reflected wave to a minimum, the rear wall must be heavily damped with absorbents or damping pads, it being of greater importance here than anywhere else.

Considerations

It can be seen from all this then, that producing an infinite baffle speaker is no means a case of simply mounting a driver or two in a sealed box, although that is how some speaker manufacturers appear to view it. Many parameters have to be considered in order to get the design right and even then reputable makers often have to make many trial-and-error

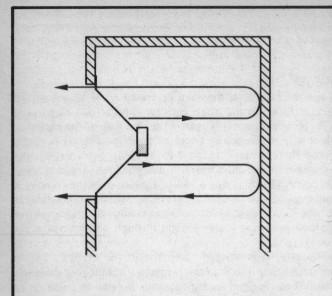

Fig. 21. Pressure wave from rear of the speaker cone is reflected from rear wall of the enclosure and passes right through the cone to emerge delayed and so out of phase with the original.

modifications to the prototype before the speaker is released on to the market.

Generally, the smaller the speaker the tighter are the tolerances and the greater the effect of small errors. A real problem is the decision to opt for either an apparently extended bass or a smooth bass, then design for the required Q. The difficulties in subduing the dimensional and panel resonances inherent with sealing up a hefty sound pressure wave in an airtight box also must be met; rather like sealing a genie in a bottle! If all these problems are successfully tackled, good results can be obtained.

There is though one remaining inherent disadvantage with the airtight enclosure for which there is no real solution. It can best be understood by comparison with a bicycle pump. If you slide the extended handle of a bicycle pump inward with the exit hole free, what little resistance it meets is the same along its whole travel. If now you do the same with a finger pressed over the exit hole, the resistance though slight to start with gets progressively greater until it is virtually impossible to push the handle the last few inches. The reason is because the internal air pressure increases with the inward travel of the handle.

A similar principle applies to a loudspeaker cone working against the air in a sealed box; there is little resistance to the initial cone movement, but as the cone travels further inward, the internal pressure rises and offers an increasing back pressure. According to Newton's Laws of Motion, the movement of a body is the result of all the forces acting upon it. So, the cone excursion is progressively reduced the further it travels. Its motion is not soley dependant on the applied signal as it is with a speaker on an open baffle. There is a similar effect when the cone moves outward, but now it is creating an increasing vacuum as it does, so its outward excursion is likewise inhibited (Fig. 22).

The result is a non-linear response to the applied signal. However, at mid and high frequencies, the cone has completed its excursion and is moving in the opposite direction before the pressure has had time to build up and exert a back force. So at these frequencies, there is little audible effect, but at lower ones that are in the bass register, non-linear back pressure causes high harmonic distortion. The larger the cabinet the lower the frequency at which non-linear back pressure starts having an effect, so small cabinets suffer the most.

Overall then, the sealed box speaker can produce deeper bass than any other of similar size, but at best the bass will have high harmonic distortion, and at worst will have boom and sundry other colorations along with it.

Wall Speakers

A step closer the true infinite baffle is the loudspeaker set into a dividing wall between two rooms. Most of the problems discussed above disappear. The speaker should be mounted on a small wooden sub-baffle and set halfway through the thickness of the wall. It should not be mounted so that there is a cavity in front. The main problem is likely to be a social one,

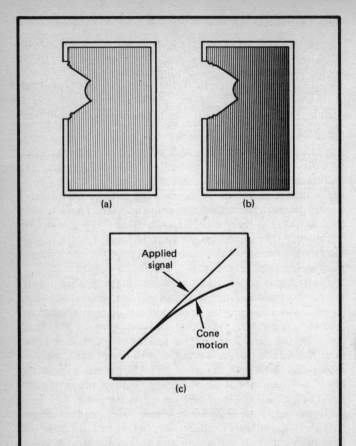

Fig. 22. When the cone moves inward in a sealed enclosure (a) pressure increases (b) exerting an opposing force in the cone. It thus does not follow the applied signal at the extremities of cone excursion (c), adding distortion. The effect occurs only at low frequencies.

would the occupants of the room next door be happy with the idea, especially as the stereo would be in reverse?

Reflex Enclosure

The reflex enclosure is airtight like the infinite baffle, except
for a small vent or *port* at the front through which some of the
rear sound can escape. Usually, the port has a small inlet pipe
penetrating into the enclosure. The basic principle behind this
is that the rear wave is delayed and so emerges 180° later at
certain frequencies which makes it in phase with the front wave
thereby reinforcing it (Fig. 23).

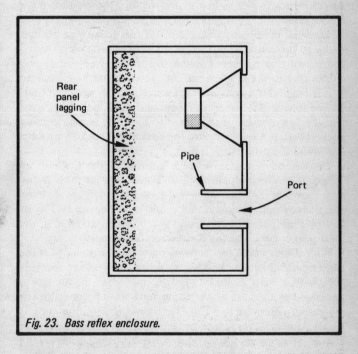

Fig. 23. Bass reflex enclosure.

The air in the inlet pipe is isolated from the rest of the air in
enclosure except at its inside end. It has inertia and so has a
resonant frequency of its own which is largely independant of
that in the enclosure. the pipe is so proportioned that its
resonant frequency is the same as that of the cone and
enclosure air combined. Having two resonant frequencies the
same may seem disastrous in view of what has previously been

said about avoiding similar cabinet dimensions to prevent such a situation. However, it is the manner in which the air masses react with each other that gives the desired effect.

At high frequencies the inertia of the air in the pipe is too great for it to respond so the enclosure behaves as if it were a totally sealed cabinet. Performance is thus similar to that of an infinite baffle at those frequencies.

Interaction at Resonances

At resonance, which is in the bass region, the pipe air mass reacts against the springiness of the enclosure air mass and vibrates but in opposite phase to it. We can get an idea of what happens by considering two pendulums of the same mass, hence swinging frequency, hung so that the free end of one strikes that of the other. The first one is driven by a force so that it maintains a constant backwards and forwards motion. At the first strike, the second pendulum is knocked outward and the first reverses then returns to meet the second coming back. There is another strike, the second is knocked outward again and the process continues.

The second pendulum is kept moving by the first but its direction is always opposite to it. So too the air mass in the pipe moves in the opposite direction to the enclosure air mass and thereby radiates sound that is out of phase with it. This of course is in phase with the sound generated by the front of the loudspeaker cone and the desired reinforcement occurs.

With the air in the pipe moving outward at resonance at the same time as the cone, the decompression inside the enclosure is greater than with an infinite baffle, and when the air moves backward it does so at the same time as the cone thereby increasing compression. Thus the movement of the cone is highly damped at resonance and its excursion is no greater than at other frequencies. This is opposite to its normal behaviour by which cone excursion is greater at resonance. It can thus handle a larger signal without driving it beyond the limits at which non-linear distortion and straining of the suspension can occur. Its power handling capacity is thereby increased.

Returning to our analogy of the pendulums, if we visualised them as being linked at their free ends with elastic or a spring, we can get a more accurate idea of what happens especially at higher frequencies. The first pendulum is made to swing much faster so that the second when struck hardly has time to move before it is being pulled back by the elastic, and when it begins to respond to this pull it is struck again. So it really doesn't know whether it is coming or going and its inertia prevents it from hardly moving at all. This is just the situation at high frequencies we described for the two air masses which are linked by their mutual elasticity. The higher the frequency the less the response of the second air mass will be.

Let us now imagine though, that the first pendulum is slowed right down. It meets the second one but instead of knocking it on it gently pushes it forward, and when it reverses, the second one does also. So, the second pendulum moves under the influence of the first as before, but this time it travels in the same direction.

This is what happens to the air mass in the pipe at frequencies below resonance. It has insufficient inertia to bounce back and it follows the same movement and direction as that of the enclosure air mass. So it behaves as a simple leak in the baffle and the rear wave emerges out-of-phase to cancel the wave from the front.

Disadvantages

The cancellation effects below resonance produce a very sharp drop in output, up to 24 dB per octave. This is partly due to the high efficiency above resonance which is around 5 dB or three times the output of an infinite baffle enclosure. The fall from this must therefore be more rapid. While the high efficiency is desirable, a rapid drop can result in 'ringing' and other unmusical effects in the bass register. A gentler slope gives better subjective results even if it starts at a higher frequency and thereby curtails the bass somewhat.

Another snag is that only the minimum amount of lagging can be used inside the enclosure because lagging reduces Q, and as the enclosure air resonance plays such an important part in the operation, a high Q is essential. Thus panel resonances and other problems resulting from insufficient lagging may be encountered. The back panel should be lagged though to prevent a reflected wave passing out through the loudspeaker cone.

As all resonant objects store energy then subsequently release it, this happens also with the reflex enclosure. Sound is thereby radiated after cessation of the input signal. This gives rise to a rather muddled effect especially on bass transients such as string bass pizzicato notes.

A further drawback with the reflex enclosure is that air turbulence is generated around the pipe and the vent which can produce noise at high volume levels. With smaller enclosures friction losses around the vent can reduce the advantage of high efficiency.

Auxiliary Bass Radiator

As an alternative to the pipe, a device similar to a dummy loudspeaker is sometimes used. It is a cone suspension without the magnet and coil, its mass serving as a substitute for that of the air in the pipe. It avoids the pipe noise and air turbulence and also serves as a barrier to mid-frequencies which may radiate through a vent from internal reflections. Its mass can be precisely designed for a specific enclosure, and it can be made to resonate at the required frequency in a smaller enclosure than would be possible with a normal vent.

Impedance

With an infinite baffle enclosure, the cone excursions are larger at resonance than at any other frequency, although the acoustic output may not be greater because of the damping introduced by a Q that is less than unity. The back emf which is generated by the coil transversing the magnetic field, is therefore also greater at resonance, as is the opposing current it produces.

Thus the total forward current (signal current minus back current) is smaller. The effective impedance of the circuit is therefore greater. A graph of the impedance of any loudspeaker in an infinite baffle enclosure will show a peak at the resonant frequency. In fact if such a graph is published with the speaker specification, one can determine the resonant frequency from it more easily than from the frequency response chart.

In the case of the reflex enclosure, the cone is physically restrained by the air loading as we have seen, so its excursion is less than it is at the surrounding frequencies. Back emf and current is thereby reduced so instead of a peak there is a dip in the impedance at resonance. However, on approaching resonance from either side, the cone starts a more vigorous motion, but it dies down at the actual resonant frequency. Thus are obtained two small impedance peaks equally spaced either side of resonance. These clearly identify a reflex speaker. (Fig. 24).

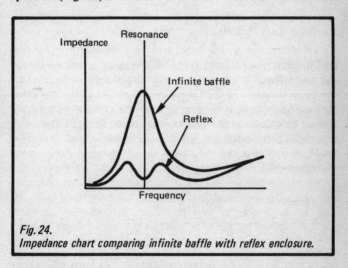

Fig. 24.
Impedance chart comparing infinite baffle with reflex enclosure.

They appear as such only when the two resonant systems are at the same frequency which is when the reflex action is working properly. With small enclosures, some designers tune the tube air mass to a slightly higher frequency than that of the enclosure, and this shows up as a pair of unequal peaks, the lower being the largest.

Enclosure Design

Construction must be sturdy of a dense material to avoid panel resonances as lagging cannot be used except over the back. The formula for calculating enclosure volume is as follows:

$$V = \pi r^2 \left(\frac{4.66 \times 10^6}{f^2 \, (L + 1.7r)} + L \right) \text{ins}^2$$

In which V is the volume of the enclosure in cubic inches; r is the radius of the speaker cone; L is the length of the tube; and f is the resonant frequency of the speaker; all measurements in inches. For this formula the area of the vent should equal that of the speaker cone.

If you prefer to work in metric units the following is an approximate equivalent, all measurements in cm.

$$V = \pi r^2 \left(\frac{304 \times 10^6}{f^2 \, (L + 1.7r)} + L \right) \text{cm}^2$$

The design is quite critical as the two resonant systems must be matched. There is though a quite simple way of tuning an enclosure to get it right. The resonant frequency of the tube depends on its length, so some means of construction must be devised which allows the length to be altered in both directions at least experimentally, until the optimum length has been determined. Once this has been done, the adjustable tube could be replaced with a permanant one of the correct length.

The tuning requires an audio oscillator, amplifier and a.c. ammeter. The oscillator does not have to be anything fancy as long as its frequency can be varied around the resonant frequency of the system. The method is to connect the speaker to the amplifier with the ammeter in series. Next feed a signal from the oscillator into the amplifier input and adjust the amplifer gain and ammeter range to get a readable indication. Now starting well above the resonant frequency, slowly sweep the frequency of the oscillator down to and below the resonant frequency.

The peaks will show up as two dips in the current reading. The important thing is to get them both the same. If they are not equal the two resonant frequencies are not matched. So, adjust the tube length until they are. As an alternative to the ammeter a voltmeter can be connected across the speaker, in which case the peaks will show as peaks and not dips. The success of using a voltmeter depends on the amplifier and how much its output voltage is dependant on the load. If the peaks are barely discernable, connect a 5-watt (or larger) wire-would resistor in series with the amplifier and speaker. Almost any value between 5 and 100 ohms will do.

Summary

The reflex enclosure enjoyed popularity in the early days of hi-fi because it had a greater bass response than unsealed cabinets, and a higher output than sealed ones. The latter was important in the days of small valved amplifiers. Furthermore the acoustic suspension speaker and infinite baffle sealed enclosure had not then been developed to their present stage.

When they came along, and amplifier powers began to climb, the reflex speaker fell from favour. Its indistinct boomy bass so long a part of the hi-fi scene, was at last recognised for what it was. However, of recent years some manufacturers have developed the reflex system, using various devices including acoustic resistance in the vent to reduce turbulance and the rapid bass roll-off, along with methods of minimising panel resonances. The result has been speakers giving quite creditable results and a much cleaner bass than their early ancestors.

For the home designer without their experience and equipment though, the reflex enclosure poses rather too many pitfalls. It should be built only on one of two conditions. Either by following exactly the plans supplied by a reputable speaker unit manufacturer, or purely as a design exercise to try out ideas. In the latter case, the previously mentioned formulae and test method can be used as a starting point.

The Horn

From ancient times the special properties of the horn as an acoustic amplifier have been appreciated and used. It was discovered early that a hollow animal horn would amplify the voice or make quite a loud musical sound, hence no doubt the origin of the name. It has been used widely in musical wind instruments, and also for public-address systems. It is also used for some hi-fi reproducers.

The horn has one major advantage over all other types of speaker system. It also has one major disadvantage. To understand these we need to know just what effect a horn has. In the case of a loudspeaker cone we have a large mass impelled by a considerable force used to move a slice of air of the same area which is very light. This is like the proverbial sledgehammer being used to crack a walnut, or, an illustration we have used before, driving a car at high speed along a flat road in bottom gear.

If the loudspeaker cone is placed at the beginning of a duct that has an increasing area along its length, it first moves a slice of air of small area. This moves an adjacent one of slightly larger area, which moves one that is larger still, and so on. The final large slice actuates the free air at the end of the duct.

Efficiency

Thus the action of the cone is smoothly and progressively matched to the eventual low impedance of the free air. The device is in fact an acoustic transformer, with the force exercised by the cone being applied to maximum effect. As a result of this, remarkable efficiencies can be obtained of over 80% this comparing with less than 1% for most infinite baffle speakers. So the theoretical output can be well over eighty times that of a sealed box speakers, or conversely, quite a small amplifer of just 1 watt would be more than adequate for domestic purposes.

The advantage in this is not just a cheaper amplifier. It is quite easy to design a high quality amplifier using class A output stages to provide a couple of watts. It is when high powers are needed that the problems start. To avoid massive heat dissipation, class B operation is commonly used, but this generates third harmonic crossover distortion. Various ploys are used to minimise this. Most vary the transistor bias according to signal amplitude so that at high levels at which crossover distortion is least noticeable, the output stage operates in class B, but at low levels it is biased to class A.

Other arrangements have been employed such as feedforward, current dumping, and pulse-width modulation, with varying degrees of success. Some of these produce very low *measured* distortion, but often still lack the clean musical sound of pure class A. All are just trying to get class A quality at high power. If then a loudspeaker is so efficient as to enable a low power class A amplifier to be used, this can be considered a major advantage.

Flares

The manner by which the horn increases in area can affect its performance. The simplest configuration is a cone, but it is by no means the best. Reflections can occur between the sides which cause interference and irregular frequency response as well as distortion. The ideal is an exponential horn by which the area increases according to an exponential law (Fig. 25). This gives optimum air load matching and prevents internal reflections.

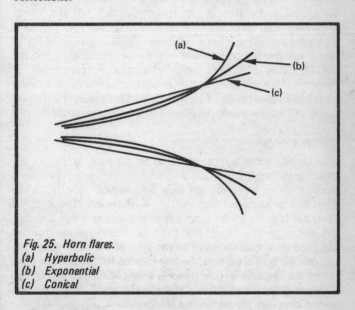

Fig. 25. Horn flares.
(a) Hyperbolic
(b) Exponential
(c) Conical

Because there is a mathematical law governing the expansion of area, it follows that there is a fixed relationship between the length of the horn and the size of the flare at its end. A large flare must have a long passage leading to it.

Another factor related to size is the frequency response. The shortest wavelength that the horn will reproduce is twice the diameter of the throat or start of the horn. The longest wavelength it will radiate is equal to twice the flare diameter. It is this last fact that gives rise to the big disadvantage. To obtain a response down to 100 Hz, a flare of 5.6 ft (1.7m) is required. For a 50 Hz response it would have to be 11.2 ft across.

The length of the horn needed for a specified flare and throat area is given by:

$$L = \frac{\log A - \log a \times 4,000}{f \times \log_e}$$

In which L is the length of the horn in cm; A is the area of the flare, and a the area of the throat in cm^2; f is the lowest frequency; $\log_e$ is 0.4343.

A horn following a hyperbolic area increase gives a response to a lower frequency than that of the exponential horn, but the roll-off below it is more rapid. The area increase from the throat is more gradual, so the sound pressure is greater there, to fall off more rapidly near the flare. This pressure variation along the length results in distortion being generated.

Throat Design

The throat needs to be of as small an area as practically possible in order to obtain a good high frequency response, because as we have already seen the shortest wavelength the horn will produce is twice the throat diameter. However, the cone needs to be larger than this in order that it will function effectively, so this means that the area immediately in front of the cone must narrow down to the start of the horn proper. A region of high pressure is thereby created in front of the cone which could cause it to respond in a non-linear fashion and so produce distortion. To avoid this the pressure is equalised by a sealed chamber placed behind the cone.

Another problem is that sound pressure from the central and outer areas of the cone could arrive at the centrally located throat at slightly different times because of the difference in spacing from it. Cancellation effects at various frequencies could thereby occur. This is prevented by introducing a plug with holes in it in front of the cone to delay some of the pressure waves so that they all arrive at the throat at the same time.

Domestic Hi-Fi Horns

Most of the design details we have discussed relate to the long metal public-address horns often seen in sports stadiums and other outdoor locations. We have done so in order to show what principles are involved and the problems that are encountered when attempting to use the horn for domestic hi-fi. When listening to public-address horns, one fact is inescapable, they are very much lacking in bass because of the limited length and area of the flares. Even so, the horns are much bigger than most people would like to accomodate in their living rooms.

As we saw in an earlier chapter, horns are used successfully in front of tweeters to improve the efficiency of those such as the ribbon, that have a low acoustic output. It is the bass frequencies that causes the problems.

Some public-address horns are folded back on themselves in a configuration termed a *re-entrant* horn. This helps with the length but does nothing to reduce the size of the flare. Some form of folding is the only way a horn could be used domestically.

The usual arrangement is to mount the driver facing forward in a large cabinet. It is the rear wave that is horn loaded by forming a path of approximately exponentially increasing area by means of a system of wooden partitions. The path so formed is folded to make best use of the available space within the cabinet, and finally terminates in a large flare opening (Fig. 26). The partitions do not have to be lagged, as the sound pressure waves do not meet them head on as they do with sealed enclosures, but travel parallel to them. In fact lagging would destroy the smooth progressive nature of the path.

One problem that is overcome by this method is the production of high frequencies. These are radiated directly by the front of the speaker and so are not limited by the area of the throat or start of the passage. It would be difficult to

71

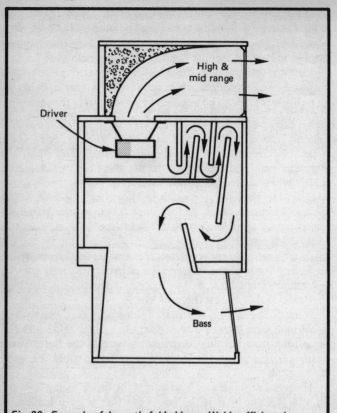

Fig. 26. Example of domestic folded horn. Highly efficient, low distortion, but large and tricky to manufacture.

obtain a small throat area using a normal bass driver, and a chamber so formed would be highly resonant and so colour the reproduction.

Any such design using wooden partitions however ingenious, cannot follow a true exponential law, and as a result efficiency suffers. This is not a major drawback through, as efficiencies of 40% are common which still compares very

72

favourably with every other type of enclosure. More serous are the reflections which can produce colorations. However, with a good design, these are not too serious, and the horn sounds cleaner than most infinite baffles or reflex enclosures.

The major problem though remains: size versus bass response. Some models are designed with a rear opening so that the flare size can be augmented by mounting the enclosure tight across a corner of the room. The walls are thereby used as an extension of the horn. The shape is quite wrong, but a useful improvement in bass response can thereby be achieved.

Transmission Line, Labyrinth

The transmission line or labyrinth type of enclosure has many advantages over other types of enclosure, but like all the others has some practical disadvantages too. It gets its name from the electrical transmission line used to convey audio or video signals. If the end of such a line is left unconnected signals travelling along it are reflected back to the source from the open end. In the case of video signals, a monitor connected at some point along the line will exhibit 'ghosting', spurious outlines appearing on the right of all vertical objects in the picture. These are due to the reflected signals arriving back slightly later than the outgoing ones.

If though the line has a high degree of loss, or a matching circuit is connected to the end, the signal is totally absorbed and none is reflected back. As a high loss would severely attenuate the signal, the latter course is adopted by connecting a terminating resistor of the same value as the line impedance across its end. Reflections are thus eliminated.

In the case of the speaker enclosure, a long path that is filled with acoustically absorbent material is provided, down which the rear wave is sent. It thus behaves like a 'lossy' transmission line. Whatever small amount of energy reaches the end, any that may be reflected back undergoes further loss on the return journey so that little if any arrives back at the loudspeaker to modify its cone motion. Thus one of the major sources of distortion of the infinite baffle enclosure is eliminated (Fig. 27).

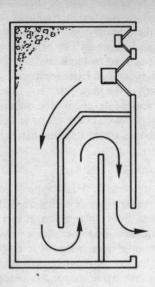

Fig. 27. Typical transmission line enclosure. The path is often tapered to reduce section resonances.

In practice the end of the line is left open so that what is left of the rear wave escapes into free air. What happens then depends on the amount of absorbent in the line. If a minimal amount is included, a fairly strong rear waves emerges, but because of the time taken to travel along the line it is in phase with the front wave and so reinforces it. This occurs when the length of the line is a quarter of the wavelength of the emerging sound.

The effect is thus similar to that of the reflex enclosure but without the strong air and possible panel resonances. An air resonance does exist but it is damped by the absorbent material and so is of a much lower Q and thus produces less coloration. The reflex enclosure on the other hand must be undamped because its operation depends on resonance.

Like the reflex system though, the bass roll-off is rapid below the quarter-wavelength frequency which is usually chosen to be at the speaker cone resonant frequency. When so chosen, the cone excursion, as with the reflex speaker, is curtailed by the air load and so permits greater power handling and less distortion at that frequency.

If alternatively, the line is well filled with absorbent material, the emerging rear wave is weak and does little to reinforce the front wave, However, the roll-off is more gentle, and if the length of the line is made slightly longer than the quarter wavelength of the cone resonant frequency, the roll-off can be extended a little lower still.

Resonant Pipe

The transmission line enclosure behaves like an organ pipe, closed at one end and open at the other. As such it has a fundamental resonant frequency which can not only colour the reproduction by over-emphasis of that frequency, but as with all resonant objects, it stores energy and releases it after the signal has ceased so giving a spurious output.

The resonance can as we have noted, be damped by filling with absorbent material. A closed pipe (closed at one end) has at resonance a node of minimum air particle motion at the closed (loudspeaker) end, and an antinode of maximum motion at the open end. Effective damping requires a greater concentration of material at the antinode where air motion is greatest, while less is required at the node. So the material should be packed more tightly at the vent.

In addition to the fundamental resonance, a pipe has harmonic resonances at multiples of the fundamental frequency. Fortunately, a closed pipe does not generate even harmonics, so second, fourth, sixth, etc. harmonics present no problem. Odd harmonics are generated though, and so need attention (Fig. 28).

The third harmonic has antinodes at the one-third and open end positions. The extra packing at the open end to dampen the fundamental will thus do the same for the third harmonic, also some extra packing at the one-third position will be required.

The fifth harmonic has antinodes at the one-fifth, three-fifths and again at the open end. Some extension of the extra

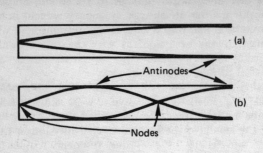

Fig. 28. Disposition of nodes (locations of minimum air motion) and antinodes (locations of maximum air motion) in a closed pipe; at (a) fundamental, and (b) 3rd harmonic.

material back from the one-third position can take care of the first antinode and the final one at the open end is already damped. A little extra just over halfway, deals with the middle one. Exact positions are not critical as the air motion varies gradually along the length from node to antinode, so somewhere near the antinode will effectively dampen it. Higher odd harmonics are weak and are suppressed by the existing absorbent.

Partitioning used to form the line is not subject to violent pressure differences from one side to the other, as in most cases the two sides are adjacent sections of the transmission line path. So panel resonances are not a problem and can be unlagged providing they are of reasonable thickness.

Sensitivity is greater than the infinite baffle though less than the non-airtight cabinet and nowhere near that of the horn. It therefore does not require a high power amplifier, moderate power is in most cases sufficient. Depending on the driver(s) chosen it may even be possible to use a low-to-moderate power class A amplifier and thereby improve results even further.

It is thus theoretically possible to get sound reproduction virtually free from air and panel resonances and non-linear cone excursion and with a natural bass response. So what are the snags?

Practical Problems

As with the horn, size is the chief concern, the rear line or passage must be at least 8 ft long, which is about a quarter wavelength of 35 Hz. However, unlike the horn it does not have to increase in area throughout its length; in fact ideally, the area should remain constant, the same as that of the speaker cone. So although an 8ft passage cuts out the possibility of a bookshelf transmission line speaker, it does not have to be quite the monster size required for a full-range horn. Even so the speakers are usually much larger than the average infinite baffle and a pair can occupy a fair amount of space.

Most of the problems arise from the necessity to fold the passage into a form that can be accommodated in a practical enclosure. One of the snags here is each section so formed tends to have a resonant frequency of its own together with harmonics. To minimise this effect, in some models the pasage is tapered so that the area gradually diminishing toward the end. This lowers the frequency of the third and fifth harmonic which in itself is not detrimental. Another effect of tapering though, is to produce back pressure which could influence cone movement and to increase the sound pressure along the length which is opposite of 'losing' it as we want. In such cases there is a substantial output from the vent so the reflex mode must apply.

Another effect is that the partitioning on the bends can reflect waves back up the previous section, and can also absorb and release energy to add coloration. However this and the individual section resonances can be greatly reduced by the efficient reflection of sound waves around the bends. If this is done effectively, the passage behaves virtually as if it was in one straight run. This is one of the problems tackled in a novel way in the Kapellmeister speakers described in the final chapter.

The provision of a long folded passage means plenty of woodwork to say nothing of design ingenuity. As a result, commercial speakers are expensive, and D-I-Y designs rather laborious and difficult to construct. These problems too have been carefully considered and minimised along with that of size in the Kapellmeisters.

Chapter 4

ABSORBENTS

Absorbents are used for two main purposes in loudspeaker enclosures, firstly to damp panel vibrations and secondly to damp internal air resonances. The panels of enclosures that are totally sealed or have a small vent to function in the reflex mode, are subject to large pressure differences between their internal and external surfaces. These can cause them to warp in sympathy and thereby themselves radiate sound. Such sound is coloured by the resonances of the panels and so adds distortion to that radiated by the loudspeaker cone.

Panel Damping

A heavy and dense absorbent layer fixed to the internal panel surfaces considerably dampens any tendency to sympathetic vibration. A comparatively light panel heavily lagged has proved less prone to vibration than a more substanial panel only lightly damped. Generally, the thicker the layer, the lower the frequency it will effectively absorb. As it is at the lower and mid frequencies that the panels resonate, only a thick or very dense layer is of any use. Various materials have been used for this purpose, but among the best so far discovered are bitumous pads.

All panels of infinite baffle speakers should be internally lagged with these, but not those of reflex cabinets as the resonance effects on which the enclosure depends could be dampened. Transmission line and folded horn partitions do not need lagging, and the operation of the horn in particular would be impaired by it.

The rear panel in the infinite baffle and reflex enclosures, is especially prone to trouble, as high pressure waves can be reflected back to the loudspeaker, and right through the cone which is virtually acoustically transparent. At frequencies when the depth of the cabinet is equal to a quarter and threequarter wavelengths, cancellation occurs, and at those corresponding to a half and whole wavelengths there is

79

reinforcement. A series of dips and peaks result, some accompanied by severe distortion.

Particular attention should therefore be paid to lagging the rear wall to avoid this effect, and even reflex enclosures which are normally unlagged should have rear wall damping.

Air Resonances

The three enclosure dimensions of a sealed enclosure have their fundamental air resonance frequencies along with harmonics (Fig. 29). To dampen these, absorbent material needs to be located at the positions of maximum air motion or the antinodes.

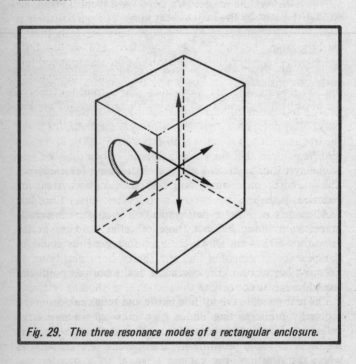

Fig. 29. The three resonance modes of a rectangular enclosure.

These antinodes are spread across numerous points in all dimensions, so the most practical course with a small enclosure is to completely fill it with absorbent. With larger enclosures the problem is to avoid compression of the lower layers by the weight of the upper ones. One method of overcoming this is to fill the lower area with several vertical rolls of material, then lay a horizontal roll across the top of these.

Reflex enclosures should not have absorbent filling as the air resonance is essential for their operation. As noted above, the only absorbent in a reflex enclosure should be on the rear wall. The folded horn also should be without absorbent as its purpose is to impart effective air motion to the outside from the movement of the loudspeaker cone. The last thing we want to do here then is to dampen that motion.

Transmission line enclosures need absorbent in the air passage though not fixed to the partitions. The purpose here is twofold, the first being to 'lose' the rear wave so that it emerges from the end greatly attenuated and so has little cancellation effect on the front wave. As the transmission line behaves as a closed pipe, it has a strong fundamental resonance along with odd harmonics. The second function of the absorbent is therefore to dampen these resonance modes. Extra density at the antinodal positions serve to do this.

Materials

A variety of materials can and have been used for enclosure filling. Polyurethane foam is a convenient one as it can be obtained in various sizes, blocks and sheet. Glass fibre has been used, but is not recommended. Its acoustic absorbent properties are inferior to other materials, and it can be a health hazard to work with. However, if nothing else is available, it can be used.

Long-fibre wool is considered the best material of all, but being loose, it is not easy to use and some method of retaining it in place must be devised. It suffers more than most from the problem of compacting under its own weight where large volumes are used. Another factor which must be considered is the need for moth-proofing if the enclosure is open such as with a transmission line.

The material most generally used because of its convenience and acoustic properties is bonded cellulose acetate fibre, commonly known as BAF wadding. It comes in sheets of 1 inch or 2 inch thickness, usually 3 ft, wide, and can be rolled up to form large wads or laid out in several thicknesses. It is quite easy to cut. It is springy and so can be compressed with extra thicknesses at antinodal points, but its density is normally about right for general filling. Over compression can result in too great a density with a reduction of the actual air volume.

BAF should be used wherever possible. It is supplied by the specialist loudspeaker firms such as Wimslow Audio and is available by mail order. It may be difficult to obtain locally, as it is only specialist shops that stock it.

Adiabatic Propagation

When a sound wave travels through air it is assisted by self-generated heat. It is a well-known fact that pressure produces heat. So the regions of pressure within the wave generate corresponding regions of higher temperature. These expand, thereby increasing the pressure and producing more heat. The sound wave quickly passes and the regions at different temperatures soon merge, so there is no lasting effect at any static point in the path of the sound wave.

However, the pressure wave carries a wave of higher temperature with it, the region of high pressure always being at a higher temperature than the mean air temperature. Now the velocity of a sound wave varies with temperature, being greater at higher values. So the velocity of the pressure wave is actually increased by its self-generated heat. The propagation is said to be *adiabatic*, which means impervious to heat change.

As this is the normal way whereby sound is propagated it is allowed for in our acoustic calculations and is not usually necessary to consider it. It is when conditions differ from this, that we need to take it into account.

Isothermal Propagation

When a sound pressure wave travels through a medium which conducts heat more readily than air which is a very poor conductor, the higher temperature regions lose heat more quickly to the surrounding lower temperature areas. Thus the temperature is not maintained and in fact never reaches the value that it would have done in air. The result is that the sound velocity is slower than in air. The condition is termed *isothermal* which literally means 'of the same heat' as adjacent regions do not have the temperature differences of the adiabatic condition.

Absorbent material such as BAF, although not seeming to be a good conductor of heat, conducts it better than air. So sound generated in a loudspeaker enclosure filled with an absorbent is propagated in partly isothermal conditions. It is thereby slowed down.

This has a useful bonus effect. The time taken to travel across a filled enclosure is longer, so the enclosure therefore appears to be larger to the sound wave. We thus get the same effect from an absorbent filled enclosure that we would from a larger one that was unfilled.

Unfortunately the difference is not large; for a fully isothermal state, the reduction in sound velocity is $\sqrt{2}$ or 1.414, giving the effect of an enclosure that much larger in volume. This would reduce the resonant frequency to about 0.833 of its former value, a very useful reduction. However, the effect of the absorbent is to create an only partly isothermal condition, much depending on the material and the packing density. It is interesting to speculate what effect fine copper wires spun into the material may have in increasing the effect to nearly full isothermal propagation.

Chapter 5
CROSSOVER NETWORKS

It is common practice to employ separate drivers to handle the treble and bass frequencies, and sometimes the mid frequencies too. Occasionally a sub-woofer is used to extend the bass about an octave below that of the bass driver. A separate enclosure is needed for this and because we cannot determine the location of very low frequencies, a single unit supplied from both stereo channels is usually effective. Super tweeters are sometimes used to extend the response well beyond the content of most programme material and beyond the human audibility range too.

An essential requirement in such multiple driver systems is a circuit for separating the frequency bands that feed the different drivers. These are known as *crossover networks* and consist of an arrangement of two basic components, a capacitor and an inductor or coil.

Capacitive Reactance

Firstly, let us consider exactly what a basic capacitor is. It consists of two conductors having a large area in close proximity to each other. When a voltage source is connected across it, electrons are drawn from one surface and rush through the source to the other. There is thus a deficiency on the first and a surplus on the second. The capacitor is then said to be charged and if the source is disconnected, a voltage equal to that of the source can be measured across the capacitor.

Charging a capacitor is not like filling a bottle, in that once it is full it will accept no more. If the source voltage is increased, the charge will increase right to the point when the insulation between the surfaces breaks down. It is more like inflating a balloon which will take more and more until finally it bursts.

At the instant of connecting the capacitor to the source, the current flow is large as there is virtually no opposition to it. But as it becomes charged, its rising internal potential opposes that of that source thus reducing the charging current. This decreases until the internal potential and source voltage are equal, at which point it ceases. The charging curve is therefore not linear but exponential.

If removed from the source and applied to an external load, the capacitor will discharge in a similar manner, the current decreasing as the potential falls. Even without an external load, a capacitor will discharge itself in time because of internal leakage through the imperfect insulation.

If a capacitor is partly charged, and then the source voltage is reversed, it will discharge and begin to charge to the opposite polarity. If the source is again reversed before the recharge is complete, it will discharge once more and start a further charge to its original polarity. This process can be kept going indefinitely, with current flowing in and out at each polarity reversal.

So an a.c. source will keep current flowing, providing the reversals occur before the capacitor is fully charged. It should be noted that as the maximum current flows before the voltage starts to rise, maximum current and voltage do not occur at the same time. The current leads the voltage by 90°.

If the reversals are very rapid, charging and discharging will always take place at the start of the curve where the current is greatest. If reversals are slow, the capacitor will be well charged and the current be reducing before the next reversal comes. So, the average current passing through a capacitor is dependant on how rapid the reversals are. In other words, the magnitude of the current depends on the frequency of the a.c. source, the higher the frequency, the greater the current.

It also depends on the size of the capacitor. One having a large capacitance takes longer to charge and discharge, and so will still be operating at the early high-current portion of its curve at the slower low frequencies. The larger the capacitance then, the higher the current.

Both frequency and capacitance are therefore factors governing the current flow through a capacitor. They are combined in the property termed *Capacitive Reactance*, symbol X_c, which is to a capacitor what resistance is to a resistor, hence the unit is the ohm, Formula for calculating it is:

$$\frac{1}{2\pi fC}$$

where f = frequency in Hz, and C = capacitance in Farads. For microfarads the formula becomes:

$$\frac{10^6}{2\pi fC}$$

The capacitor thus offers a high impedance to low frequency signals and a low impedance to high frequencies so enabling it to be used as an element in frequency selective filter circuits.

Inductive Reactance

When a current flows through a straight wire, a circular magnetic field surrounds it which is made up of individual lines of force. If the wire is wound in the form of a coil, the lines link up to produce a concentrated field which form loops passing radially through the centre of the coil and around its exterior.

When the current starts to flow, the field does not appear instantaneously, but rapidly builds up from zero. Likewise when the current ceases, it collapses. In both instances the lines of force cut across the windings of the coil. It is this action that gives the coil its peculiar property.

Whenever a magnetic line of force cuts across a conductor, it induces an electromotive force (EMF) in it. This is the principle on which all electric generators depend. It matters not whether the conductor moves or the magnetic field, nor does it matter whether the field is produced by a permanent magnet or an electromagnet.

It follows that when the field produced by a coil builds up or collapses and so cuts across its own windings, an EMF is induced in them. This always *opposes* the original voltage that produced the current, because its polarity is opposite to it. Thus the effective voltage acting in the circuit is that of the applied voltage minus the self-induced voltage.

In the case of a d.c. supply, the effect is momentary. When the current starts to flow, the opposing EMF inhibits it so that it builds up slowly to its maximum. After this, the field is stationary and so has no effect. On removing the applied voltage the EMF generated by the collapsing field tries to perpetuate the current. Quite high voltages can be induced by the collapsing field.

With a.c., the field is constantly changing and so the current is continuously opposed. This is the property which is termed *Inductive Reactance*. Because the current builds up slowly it lags behind the applied voltage by 90° so maximum current and voltage do not occur at the same time.

The opposing or back EMF is proportional to the speed of the changing field, being highest when the speed is greatest. As the rate of change increases with frequency, it follows that the reactance is not constant but increases as the frequency rises.

It is also dependent on the inductance of the coil. This is a rather complex factor depending on the total number of turns, the turns per inch, length and diameter of the coil and the number of layers. Also affecting inductance is whether the coil is air-cored, is iron-cored (increases inductance) or is brass-cored (decreases inductance). The latter applies when brass slugs are used for tuning r.f. coils. The formula for inductive reactance is:

$$X_L = 2\pi fL$$

In which X_L is in ohms, $f =$ frequency in Hz, and L is inductance in henries.

The inductive action of a coil is reduced by its d.c. resistance so dividing the reactance by the resistance gives a quality (Q) factor. The formula then is:

$$Q = \frac{X_L}{R}$$

Thus at low frequencies the inductor offers minimum impedance, but at high frequencies the impedance is also high. Along with the capacitor which has the opposite effect, it thus affords a means of separating an audio signal into bands suitable for driving multi-speaker systems.

First-Order Network

Combinations of inductors and capacitors are arranged to provide *low-pass*, *high-pass*, or *band-pass* characteristics.

These are used to supply the bass driver, treble unit, and mid-range speaker respectively.

The simplest circuit is of a single capacitor connected in series with the tweeter. This prevents low frequencies reaching the tweeter which would seriously damage it. Both low and high frequencies are fed to the bass unit which will reproduce some of the highs due to cone flexure. Having two speakers reproducing high frequencies in close lateral proximity will result in interference at certain angles, reinforcement taking place at some frequencies and cancellation at others. Because of this the circuit is used only in cheap radio units, but it can be and is used effectively with co-axial speakers where the tweeter is mounted within the bass cone.

To avoid interference effects, an inductor is connected in series with the bass unit which filters out the high frequencies, so we have a capacitor feeding the tweeter and an inductor supplying the woofer. This is known as a *first-order* network each leg attenuating the signal outside of its pass range at the rate of 6 dB per octave (Fig. 30).

The point where they overlap is known as the *crossover frequency* and the values of the components are chosen so that at this point the response of each driver is -3 dB or half power. As we saw earlier, current through a capacitor leads the voltage, whereas it lags through an inductor. In the first-order network, the lead and lag is 45° so cancelling to produce an in-phase signal from the drivers at the crossover frequency (Fig. 31). The two half-power signals thus add to produce full power and so the response through the crossover region is flat. The formula for calculating the theoretical values are:

$$L = \frac{Z \times 10^3}{2\pi f_c} \qquad\qquad C = \frac{10^6}{2\pi f_c Z}$$

In which L is the inductance in millihenries; C is the capacitance in microfarads; Z is the speaker impedance; and f_c is the crossover frequency.

There is a snag here though. The 6 dB per octave roll off is too gentle. It means that at two octaves from the crossover point, both drivers are handling a -12 dB signal that is outside

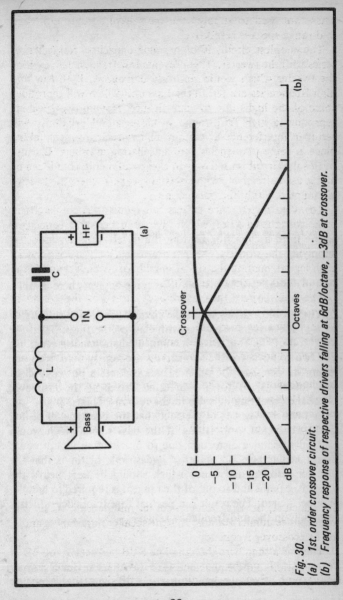

Fig. 30.
(a) 1st. order crossover circuit.
(b) Frequency response of respective drivers falling at 6dB/octave, −3dB at crossover.

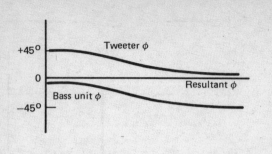

Fig. 31. Phase angles of tweeter and bass unit in 1st. order network. Resultant is zero phase shift.

of their respective bands, while at three octaves there is still a − 18 dB signal.

The problem arises when the natural frequency roll-off of one of the drivers coincides with that of the filter. Then the total roll-off for that driver is augmented and made steeper. So the two roll-offs for the two drivers are non-symmetrical, one being steeper than the other. This produces a power level of less than − 3 dB for the affected driver at the crossover frequency resulting in a dip in the response (Fig. 32).

A further snag lies in the fact that the tweeter will be fed with substantial proportions of the bass signal which would not only produce distortion due to overloading it, but could result in damage. Yet another undesirable factor is that the tweeter resonant frequency which should be kept below the crossover point and so out of the range it is required to handle, can be excited. The result is a peak at that frequency which is generally in the mid-frequency range.

Higher Orders

The solution to these problems is to use filters having a sharper roll-off. A 12 dB per octave characteristic can be obtained by

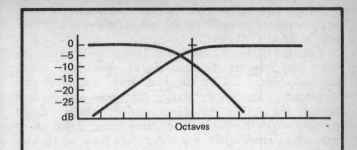

Fig. 32. The natural roll-off of the base unit can accentuate that of the crossover circuit to produce an assymetrical response with a deeper trough at crossover point below –3dB level.

adding a capacitor across the bass driver and an inductor across the tweeter. This circuit is a *second-order* network (Fig. 33), and it is also known as an L-filter because the series and parallel components form an L when drawn in a circuit diagram.

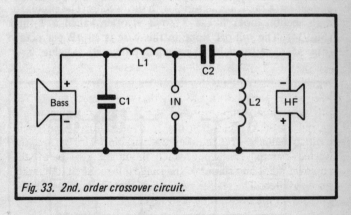

Fig. 33. 2nd. order crossover circuit.

The disadvantage is that the phase difference between the drivers is 180° which produces a dip in the response at the crossover frequency. This can be avoided by reverse connecting the tweeter, but then a hump is produced instead.

91

A further effect is that all the high frequencies are in an opposite phase relationship to the low, compared to what they were in the original signal.

A musical instrument that is rich in harmonics such as the cello, may have its fundamental and perhaps its second harmonic reproduced by the bass driver and the higher harmonics by the tweeter. Having the tweeter reversed thus changes the relationship and subsequent resultant sound pressure waveform. While the evidence is that this seems to have little audible effect, it is a departure from the tenet of hi-fi that the reproduced signal should correspond as closely as possible to the original.

Sometimes a resistor is included in series with the tweeter and its series capacitor. This is done to attenuate its output when the tweeter sensitivity is greater than that of the bass driver which is often the case. Sensitivities are thus matched to give a uniform response. A bonus effect of this is to reduce the amount of current lead through the tweeter due to the capacitor, and thus the phase difference between the two drivers.

Further components can be added to form a *third-order* network. This has an extra inductor in series with the bass unit and an extra capacitor in series with the tweeter. The circuit for each section looks like a T so it is often called a T-filter (Fig. 34). The roll-off slope in this case is 18 dB per octave (Fig. 35). The formula for calculating theoretical values is:

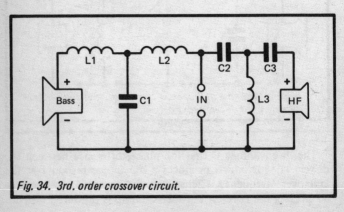

Fig. 34. 3rd. order crossover circuit.

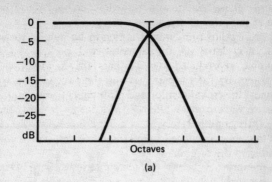

(a)

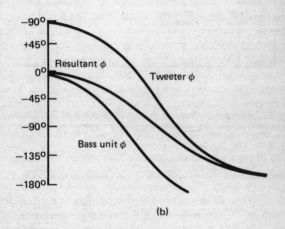

(b)

Fig. 35.
(a) Frequency response of 3rd. order drivers falling at 18dB/octave.
(b) Phase angles of drivers with resultant.

$$L_1 = 3L_2 = 2L_3 = \frac{3Z \times 10^3}{4\pi f_c}$$

and

$$C_1 = 2C_2 = \frac{2C_3}{3} = \frac{20^6}{3\pi f_c Z}$$

Adding another capacitor across the bass driver and a further inductor across the tweeter forms a fourth-order filter. This looks like the Greek letter π in the circuit and so is called a π filter (Fig. 36). It has a roll off of 24 dB per octave. As with the second-order filter there is a 180° phase reversal so the tweeter can be reverse connected unless other components are included which affect the phasing. Fourth-order filters are rarely used for crossover networks; second and third being the most common.

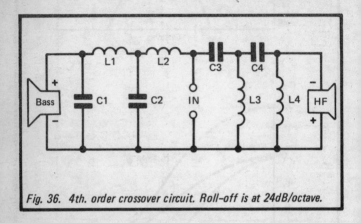

Fig. 36. 4th. order crossover circuit. Roll-off is at 24dB/octave.

The previous formulae assume that the driver impedance is constant which is not the case, it varies with frequency and resonances. They should therefore be considered as a starting point, and the values be modified according to the response of the driver. Sometimes irregularities in the response of the drivers can be partly compensated for by extra components, usually resistors across or in series with the main filter components, but additional inductors and capacitors are often used as well (Fig. 37). It is thus possible to achieve a very flat response for a particular pair of drivers and enclosure. With so many variable factors the design frequently needs to be carried out by computer.

For any published design therefore, neither the type of drivers nor values of the network should be changed. They have, or should have been, carefully optimised. It follows that

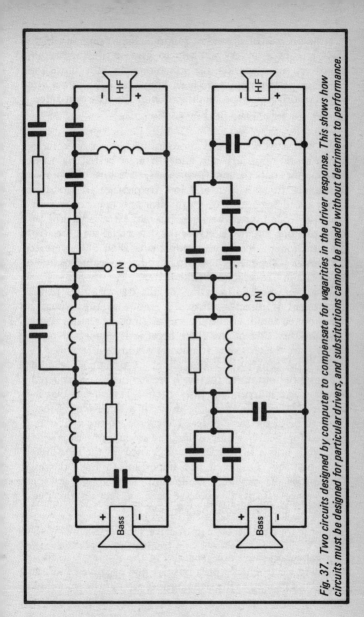

Fig. 37. Two circuits designed by computer to compensate for vagarities in the driver response. This shows how circuits must be designed for particular drivers, and substitutions cannot be made without detriment to performance.

choosing a pair of drivers at random, then using an off-the-shelf crossover is very unlikely to give satisfactory results. However, some speaker manufacturers do little more than that, and certain ones have been known to substitute a quite different driver with no modification of the crossover filter at all, for the sole reason of lower cost.

Band-pass Filters

When a mid-range driver is added it must be fed via a filter that supplies only the mid frequencies, so it must offer a rising impedance to both high and low frequencies. A first-order bandpass filter consists of a capacitor and inductor in series, while a second-order network has an extra capacitor and inductor, one in parallel across the driver and the other from the junction of the series components (Fig. 38). Here too additional components are often added to compensate for vagaries in the response of the driver.

Whatever the configuration of the network, no parallel component is directly across the input as this would be shunting the amplifier output. Any attenuating resistors are on the amplifier side of the filter because if connected on the driver side, the crossover frequency would be affected.

A further convention is that all inputs are in parallel across the amplifier output so that each section may be considered a separate and independant filter circuit. This means that it is not necessary for both or the three, if a three-way system is used, to be of the same order. Thus a second-order filter may be used for the treble unit to limit the amount of bass it will be fed, while only a first-order circuit is used for the bass driver, as it may be considered less important to limit the high frequencies it handles. While this may result in some interference effects as we have seen, it reduces the phase difference and the effects of 'ringing'

Components

The capacitors used are generally in the range of 1−10 μF. Polarised electrolytics with a positive and negative connection should not be used as the signal is pure a.c.. Furthermore, they have a wide tolerances and so a precise value cannot be

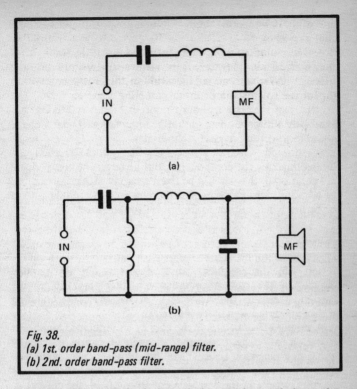

Fig. 38.
(a) 1st. order band-pass (mid-range) filter.
(b) 2nd. order band-pass filter.

obtained. Non-polarised electrolytics can be used, but other types are preferable.

It may then be wondered why a polarised electrolytic is used for coupling the output stage to the speaker circuit. The reason is that there is d.c. on the output-stage side, on which the signal is superimposed. So the actual voltage across the capacitor never reverses. Its value is not critical because it is not in a frequency selective circuit.

The inductors can be either air-cored or ferrite cored. The ferrite components are smaller because they are magnetically more efficient, most of the generated flux being concentrated in the windings by the core. The disadvantage is that it is possible for the core to saturate at high signal levels thereby varying the inductance, hence also the impedance. The result is harmonic distortion and changing of the crossover characteristics.

Air-cored inductors do not suffer from this possibility, but they are larger and heavier. A problem can arise from the large leakage field which can interact with any other inductor within range and so introduce mutual coupling between them. The effects can be strange and unpredictable. All coils but especially air-cored ones, should be mounted well apart, and if possible with their axes at right-angles.

A printed circuit board is the usual method of interconnecting the components, but however the components are connected, they should be fixed securely with no possibility of adjacent ones touching and thereby able to produce buzzes or rattles when subject to high level sound waves.

Ringing

If the signal applied across a capacitor ends abruptly, a charge is left which subsequently discharges through any parallel circuit. In the case of a crossover filter this will almost certainly include the associated driver. Thus terminating transients in the signal are blurred.

A similar effect occurs in the case of an inductor. An abrupt cessation of current flowing through it causes a rapidly collapsing magnetic field which cuts across its own windings. This generates a voltage that produces a current through any parallel circuit. In the case of a collapsing field, the current so produced is of the same polarity as the original. So the effect is to sustain the current after the signal has ceased. Again a blurring of terminating transients results.

By themselves these overhang affects may not be too bad, but there is worse to follow. The induced current in the inductor recharges the capacitor, which when the current ceases, discharges back through the inductor. So another field builds up which when it collapses, produces further current to recharge the capacitor again.

Thus current surges backwards and forwards in oscillatory cycles until the losses in the circuit reduce it to zero. The effect which is known as *ringing*, is greatest at the crossover frequency and can be clearly seen on tone-burst oscilloscope traces (Fig. 39). It it also greater with the higher order filters

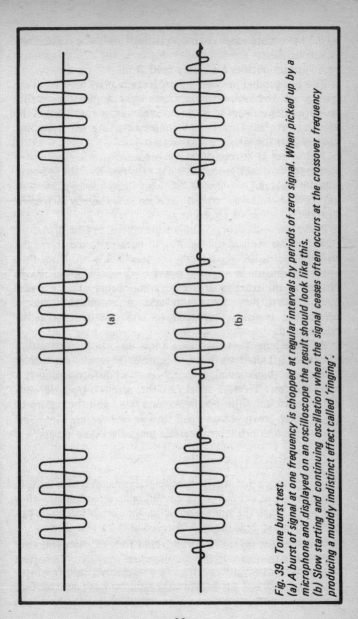

Fig. 39. Tone burst test.
(a) *A burst of signal at one frequency is chopped at regular intervals by periods of zero signal. When picked up by a microphone and displayed on an oscilloscope the result should look like this.*
(b) *Slow starting and continuing oscillation when the signal ceases often occurs at the crossover frequency producing a muddy indistinct effect called 'ringing'.*

which have more reactive components. This is one reason why first-order filters are sometimes employed for bass drivers and fourth-order circuits are rarely used at all.

There is another possible effect. Negative feedback from the output of the amplifier is commonly applied to earlier amplifier stages. Any spurious harmonics generated within the loop are thus fed back out of phase and so are self-cancelling as they pass through the final stages.

The effect is to considerably reduce distortion generated within the feedback loop, but it can only do this if the fed-back signal is truly out of phase at 180°, any delay causes phase shift and could even turn into positive feedback thereby increasing distortion instead of reducing it.

Now, the oscillatory voltages generated by the crossover filter, appear at the amplifier output terminals, and so are fed back to the earlier stage along the feedback path. They thus appear amplified in negative phase back at the output stage. However, the reactive crossover components cause a phase shift so that they arrive too late to cancel the original oscillation. Instead, they tend to make matters worse by adding to it.

So some amplifiers that have a low distortion specification on paper achieved by heavy negative feedback, can sound worse than those having higher theoretical distortion due to a more modest feedback level. As the precise effect depends both on the amplifier feedback conditions and the nature of the speaker crossover network, this is one reason why some speakers sound better with certain amplifiers than others.

Cone Oscillation Damping

Another reason for many matching anomalies and a further shortcoming of the crossover circuit, is its effect on amplifier damping. When the signal ceases the cone tends to oscillate to and fro for several cycles before coming to rest due to the springiness of the suspension. Spurious sounds are thus generated.

These cone oscillations generate a back EMF that produces current which sets up a magnetic field around the coil that opposes the cone motion. The oscillations are thus self-dampening. The same effect reduces peaks in the speaker frequency response. If the cone motion at one frequency is greater than that of the others for the same input level, the back EMF and current is also larger. So the opposing force is greater and the excess cone motion is reduced.

The only path for the back current is through the amplifier output stage. As the damping depends on the back current, it also depends on the total resistance it has to encounter, the lower the resistance the better.

A figure is often quoted in amplifier specifications for *damping factor*. This describes the ability of the amplifier to dampen spurious speaker cone motion by providing a low resistance shunt path. Output stage internal resistance is much lower than the specified output impedance, and the damping factor is the ratio between the two. Factors of 20 are nowadays considered low, and some go as high as 1,000. Taking a typical damping factor of 100 and the usual 8 ohm load, this gives an internal resistance of $8 \div 100 = 0.08$ Ω. Connected directly across a driver, such a low resistance permits a high back current and very effective magnetic damping.

However, when a crossover circuit is employed, each driver has at least one component in series with it that has reactance and in some cases also a resistance, of several ohms. These effectively limit the back current and make nonsense of those high damping factors. The higher the order of the filter, the more components there are in series.

It can be seen then that the crossover network has many vices and so is generally regarded as a necessary evil. The problems and ill effects arising from a two-way crossover are bad enough, but these are greatly compounded with three or more drivers. Even experienced manufacturers often fail to get it right, which is why multi-driver speakers appear now to be going out of fashion.

One well-known maker staged a demonstration of his loudspeaker range at a London hi-fi show a few years ago. Most of the range sounded good and there was virtually no tonal difference when different models were switched in for comparison. This is how it should be, any difference in tone indicates coloration by one or both of the units being compared. The only difference a larger size should make is to give a better account of the lowest musical octave, but as this part of the scale occurs only occasionally, for much of the time the speakers are indistinguishable.

There was though one model which had a noticeably different tone and lacked the smoothness of the others. It was assumed that this was the cheapest of the range, but investigation revealed that it was in fact the dearest, and the only one to have three drivers; all the others had two.

The poor results were excused with the thought that it might have been due to the acoustics of the demonstration room or bad positioning of the loudspeakers. However, two years later, the same range was demonstrated at a different venue no doubt with different units, but the result was the same. The three-driver speaker sounded different and inferior to all the others.

Dispensing With The Crossover Network

A necessary evil it has been called, but is it really necessary? There are several different options that can be followed. One is the *electronic active crossover*. Most of the problems arise from separating the frequency bands at high power in the output circuit. As we have seen, this causes phasing differences, ringing, feedback, and impairment of amplifier damping of spurious cone motion and response peaks.

All of these are eliminated if the frequency division occurs earlier in the chain, before the main power amplifier. It can be done quite easily, but it necessitates using two amplifiers for each channel, one for bass and the other for treble. An advantage of having two amplifiers though, is that the gain of each can be adjusted to compensate for different driver sensitivities. If required, tailoring of the response can be built-in for specific drivers as with the conventional crossover filters, but an off-the-shelf crossover is likely to be quite satisfactory.

Another method of using a tweeter without a crossover is to use one of the Motorola piezo tweeters. Their impedance rises as the frequency falls, being around 1,000 ohms at 1 kHz, and increasing according to an exponential curve below that. There is thus no danger the unit being damaged by bass signals and so can be connected directly across the bass driver.

Because the impedance curve is exponential, the output drops off rapidly below about 3kHz, in one model at the rate of 24 dB per octave. If a bass driver can be selected that has a similar rapid fall-off above that frequency, all the advantages of a high order crossover filter are obtained with none of the disadvantages. In addition, response of these piezo tweeters extends up to 40 kHz, an attraction to those wishing to play the game of frequency-response one-up-manship! Of more practical importance is the low harmonic distortion of 0.75%. The level can be adjusted by means of a 200 Ω variable resistor in series with the tweeter.

This solution, in common with that of the electronic active crossover, although eliminating the loudspeaker crossover network, still suffers from the off-axis interference effects obtained by having two drivers.

These are virtually eliminated by the coaxial speaker which has two cones in which the treble cone is mounted within the cavity of the bass. A crossover circuit may be necessary, but in some cases it is no more than a single capacitor in series with the treble coil. This is possible because the coaxial cones radiate coherent sound at all angles so there are no phase differences at off-axis locations. Shadowing effects of the treble cone at mid frequencies may be experienced and also they may be internal reflections between bass cone and the treble unit with some models.

So to the final solution, which is using a single full-range driver. These rely on cone flexure whereby the central areas of the cone move independantly of the outer ones at high frequencies. The active cone area increases as the frequency falls until the whole cone moves at low frequencies. It thus performs as a tweeter, mid-range unit and bass driver all in one.

This may seem to be a backward step to the early lo-fi days when only single speakers were used and frequency reponse was limited. Uncontrolled cone flexure occured then, not by design, but as an inevitable result of using paper cones. It produced distortion and its effect on the upper frequency response was not appreciated. It was thus considered an evil to be overcome by the search for more rigid cone materials.

Since then the effect has been studied, and research carried out to produce cones in which the flexure is controlled so that the frequency range is extended to hi-fi standards with minimum distortion. The success of such units has been increased by parallel research into enclosure design.

A practical advantage they possess over separate tweeters is that the tweeter cone surround like any moving-coil unit rarely absorbs all the waves that travel outward from the cone centre. They are consequently reflected back to produce standing waves and distortion. With a full-range driver, the treble is produced only by the central cone area, so the whole of the rest of the cone serves as a buffer between it and the cone edge, just as if it were a super surround. This effectively absorbs the outward going waves, thereby eliminating reflections and giving a more accurate h.f. response.

Most of the objections to a single driver are a hangover from the early days. Loudspeaker cones made large bass excursions in unsealed cabinets due to insufficient air loading and undamped cone resonances. They thus were often driven into non-linear operation, and so when reproducing high frequencies as well, produced intermodulation distortion. Doppler distortion also occured whereby the pitch of the high frequencies was successively raised and lowered at each forward and backward bass excursion of the cone.

With bass reflex enclosures and to a lesser extent transmission line speakers, the low frequency excursions of the cone are restricted around the resonant frequency. With a well-damped infinite baffle enclosure of moderate size the cone bass excursions though greater than these, are not excessive. So, intermodulation and doppler distortion are generally below the threshold of audibility in such enclosures operating at domestic volume levels. They thus offer no real objection to the use of single full-range drivers.

Although the frequency range of a single full-range speaker is not quite as great as can be obtained from separate bass and treble units, it is not far short, and the best full-range drivers can approach the full range of human audibility. Many are actually better than some multiple driver speakers.

Really, the use of multiple drivers, desirable in the early days of hi-fi, is now far less so, and can even be considered undesirable. It has persisted as a status symbol, the 'my-speakers-have-more-drivers-than-yours' syndrome, and of course the manufacturers with an eye to business have catered for it.

So, at the expense of a slight curtailment of frequency range, all the vices of crossover networks are avoided, a fully in-phase sound propagation at all angles is achieved, maximum damping by the amplifier of spurious cone excursions and response peaks is obtained, high frequency cone standing waves are reduced, and the lack of interaction between crossover circuit and amplifier feedback loop, means that the speaker will perform well with any amplifier. Indeed a trade-off well worth considering!

Chapter 6

WHICH PARAMETERS MATTER?

'One man's meat is another man's poison'. Nowhere is it more true than in the choice of loudspeakers. What features do you look for in a loudspeaker? Very likely they will be quite different from those chosen by your neighbour.

The perfect loudspeaker, reproducing exactly the sound field obtaining at the original performance does not yet exist. Many of the requirements are incompatible when applied to practical loudspeaker design. If we want one we must sacrifice another. The designer usually tries to effect a compromise, giving us some of both as far as that is possible. One designer may favor one characteristic and so slant his design in that direction, while another may consider the other to be of greater importance.

This being so, we will consider the main parameters and how they may affect the choice of a loudspeaker. When buying a ready-made speaker the choice may be confusing, but at least you can listen to what is on offer and maybe use a pair for a trial period in your home before deciding. It is, incidentally always wise to do this, as first impressions may not endure, or the speakers may sound quite different in the acoustics of your living room, running from your amplifier, from how they sounded in the dealer's showroom.

When you consider building to a published design or even trying your hand at your own design, you have no means of telling how it will sound until he job is complete. Then it is too late to change, so it is necessary to first analyse what parameters are important to you and what design factors will produce those parameters. You are then more likely to end up with speakers that more or less satisfy your priorities.

Cost

A necessary consideration this, but not too choice-restricting, because the most costly items, the wood and the drivers do not vary much between designs of comparable power handling and size. As large savings can be made over commercial ready-made equivalents, even the more costly DIY speakers work out to be quite reasonable. Horn or transmission line speakers will be more expensive than infinite baffle or reflex enclosures because of the extra wood needed. However, most large timber merchants sell cheap off-cuts. As the partitions are concealed inside the enclosure, any grade of plywood can be used for them, and off-cuts can often be used at considerable cost saving.

Size

A consideration that overrides many others is that of size. The majority of modern living rooms can hardly be described as spacious. What space there is is usually well filled, and accommodation for two large speaker enclosures along with the amplifying/radio/disc/tape playing equipment is in most cases very limited. Of recent years there has been competition also from other home entertainment devices such as television, video recorders, computer games, along with keyboard musical instruments which are becoming more popular.

Usually, the larger the enclosure the more extended the bass response. Many small enclosures have a bass response that sounds remarkable, but the laws of physics cannot be circumvented, it is just not possible to reproduce deep bass with a small enclosure. In such cases the makers have most likely adopted a Q that gives a hump in the response at the resonant frequency. This apparantly gives plenty of bass, but closer listening reveals that it is boomy and indistinct. If the Q is so chosen that the hump is avoided, the results are more natural but the sound is rather lacking at the bottom end of the scale.

A further disadvantage of the small enclosure is that small volume of enclosed air behaves as a harder 'spring' than a large volume, against which the cone must work. So non-linearity of cone motion is greater, producing more distortion, and sensitivity is likely to be less.

So while some remarkable bookshelf designs have been produced that make the very best of the limited space available, the results cannot be compared with much larger floor standing models of comparable quality. This is true of the popular infinite baffle type, and in the case of horn or transmission line enclosures, even more space is required.

The best course then is to avoid the very small units if at all possible, and go for the largest you can accommodate that is appropriate to your room size. The latter proviso is not just a concession to necessity but has a practical basis. The amount of bass that can be fully developed in any listening room depends on the room size. The lowest frequency that can be produced is governed by the longest room dimension and is given by:

$$f = \frac{560}{d}$$

in which f is the lowest frequency, and d is the longest dimension in feet. So a 12 ft dimension limits the response to 46Hz. It follows then that throwing out other furniture to make room for large speakers that go well below the room's frequency limit does no good at all!

If the average living room space situation is analyzed though, it will found that the problem is not so much total volume as floor area. The speakers can be tall as long as they do not take up too much space on the carpet. A column-like enclosure thus offers the best prospect of large volume with small floor area, but for a sealed unit could suffer from strong pipe resonances. However, there are some good designs using this shape and the Kapellmeisters described later is one example.

Frequency Response

A wide frequency response is usually considered a top priority, and most commercial models vie with each other in getting the widest range possible in their specs. A wide range is indeed desirable and within certain limits essential for hi-fi, but it can be overdone, especially if it is at the expense of other features.

Considering the high frequencies first, these are necessary to give the brilliance and sparkle to music; they convey the sense of presence and are essential, along with correct phasing, for good stereo imaging. Without them, music sounds dull as though heard through a heavy curtain. It becomes difficult to distinguish some instruments, especially in the woodwind section.

The response needs to go a lot higher than the frequency of the highest note likely to be played, because it is the harmonics that give all these effects. These are multiples of the fundamental frequencies generated by the musical instruments and can extend nearly to the upper limit of human hearing.

Of the 24 frequency bands into which the human ear splits up all received sound and transmits them to the brain, the centre-frequency of the highest is 13.5 kHz. Its upper limit extends to about 16 kHz, but only in the young, the upper response falls over the age of 20, increasingly so over the age of 30. At 40, the 8 kHz response is some 10 dB less (a third) of what it is at 20, while at 50 it is 20 dB less. The high quality f.m. music radio broadcasts in the U.K. have as their upper limit, 15 kHz. which is thus seen to be more than adequate. The 20 kHz response of the compact disc is a case of allowing a very wide margin over the top. No one can hear that high (except the dog) and few could get within many kHz of it.

A response above 15 kHz can therefore be considered superfluous, and should certainly not be achieved at the expense of other more important things. This calls into question the use of tweeters and especially additional super-tweeters with all the drawbacks described in the last chapter.

Now to the bass region. The lowest note produced by any orchestral instrument is 29Hz, from the contra-bassoon, while piano goes down 27.5Hz. Actually, it only rarely that those instruments get down that far. When they do, spectrum analysis reveals that the fundamental is very weak anyway, and most of the character is imparted to the tone by the harmonics. The lowest harmonic which is the second, is in the above cases 55 Hz and 58 Hz respectively. The bass drum (not the tympani) is about the only orchestral instrument that really needs a deep bass response to do it justice, as it has few harmonics beyond the starting transients.

Although it may be desirable then, to reproduce down to the lowest frequencies, it is by no means essential. In fact sub-bass response can reveal rumble, record warp, and even subway trains passing near the studio! So while a bass response within

109

a few dB down to 45 Hz can be considered desirable to give depth and richness to the reproduction, little is gained by going lower. An even higher limit can often be preferable to a lower one gained at the expense of naturalness. As noted above, the listening room dimensions may not permit the propagation of bass much lower than this anyway.

Now a word about the measurements themselves. Accurate frequency response measurements are not possible unless you have a large anechoic room, that is one that completely absorbes all sound produced within it and reflects none. Only the larger speaker manufacturers and audio laboratories have such a facility. Any response measurements attempted in any other environment except an open field are wildly inaccurate due to multiple reflections causing cancellation and reinforcement at various frequencies. Just moving the measuring microphone a few inches can cause up to a 20 dB difference in the reading at one frequency and little if any at another. Furthermore the size of the room limits the lower bass response as we have noted before.

Some loudspeaker reviewers occasionally publish graphs that were made 'under typical living room conditions', meaning their own living rooms, and try to justify them by the comment that no-one listens in an anechoic room. True, but irrelevant, no-one will be listening in the reviewer's living room either, and moving the speakers or the listening position by quite a small amount can completely change the measured response.

It is possible though, to make a fairly accurate response plot by measuring each frequency several times with the microphone in a different position, and also the speaker. The readings for each are averaged and any that are wildly different are obviously the effect of interference and are rejected. The same combination of positions is used for every frequency.

The process is a long and laborious one and does not equal the accuracy of the anehoic room measurement, but it can give results that co-relate reasonably with it. It will give the overall shape and range of the plot quite accurately, if not all the individual small peaks and dips.

110

Another method of speaker response measurement in an ordinary room is the use of *pink-noise* filtered into $\frac{1}{3}$ − octave bands. This is how it works.

If an f.m. radio that does not have interstation muting is detuned, a hissing sound is heard. This is made up of random frequencies covering the whole audio frequency spectrum, just as white light is made up of all other colours. For this reason the noise is termed *white-noise*. It has on average, an equal amount of each frequency, so as each octave has double the number of frequencies as all those below it; most of the energy is concentrated in the upper octaves. This is the reason for the characteristic 'hissy' sound.

White-noise can be filtered to alter its content so that there is an equal amount of energy in each octave rather than at each frequency. It thus contains more low frequencies than white noise and so is called *pink-noise*. It is invaluable where the use of individual frequencies for measurements may be misleading. Speaker sensitivity measurements for example, need to relate to the average sensitivity to all frequencies not just to one, so pink-noise is used.

It can also be used to a limited extent for frequency response testing splitting the noise up into $\frac{1}{3}$ − octave bands, then measuring and plotting the result. Instead of a line plot on the graph paper, the response is shown as a series of blocks or bars on the graph.

The advantage is that a group of closely related frequencies are less affected by interference effects than single frequencies, so tests can be made in an ordinary room. While this is so, the result is still affected by the room acoustics due to the narrow bands used. Wider bands would be less affected, but would give a coarser resolution. As it is, the plot which consists of a bar chart, does not reveal the sharper peaks and dips in the response.

A reasonably accurate frequency response plot, however derived, can give an idea of how the speaker will sound although it does not present the whole picture. Minor deviations from a flat response plot are to be expected and have little effect on the sound, but larger ones most probably will. A hump just before a sharp bass roll-off will result in a boomy 'one note' bass; far better is a gentler slope starting higher up. Peaks in the mid-range or treble can give an artificial brilliance but be tiring to listen to for any period.

Phasing

Phase distortion, that is phase differences between frequencies that were not present in the original, do not seem to have a noticeable effect on the quality of the sound itself. They do affect the stereo image which can be blurred or even rendered totally indeterminate except for the extreme left and right positions. The distortion is produced in all, but more particularly, the higher order crossover networks. Spatial differences between tweeter and bass driver also change the phase relationship and this varies too, according to the listening angle from the front axis of the speaker.

For better stereo imaging, a single full-range speaker, co-axial speaker, or a piezo tweeter that needs no crossover circuit should be used. If a conventional tweeter is desired, a simple crossover consisting of a first order filter for the bass and a second order for the treble will minimise phase distortion as well as ringing, but there may be a frequency response anomaly around the crossover frequency.

Ringing

The oscillations caused by energy storage and release in the reactive components of the crossover circuit known as ringing can impart a muddy and indistinct effect to the sound with loss of detail. The greater the number of drivers with their own crossover points, and also the more complex the crossover filters the worse the effects are. Damping of mechanical cone overshoot and oscillation are also impaired by high order crossovers.

The answer again is a simple crossover or better still, no crossover at all. Some commercial speaker manufacturers have in the past published tone-burst photos of their speakers at various frequencies. These are short bursts of a steady sine-wave signal each followed by a short gap of silence. Ideally, the burst should end abruptly, but usually there is a half-cycle or so overshoot visible on the oscilloscope trace.

112

It is at the crossover frequencies that the ringing really shows, often with several cycles of diminishing amplitude evident before the trace subsides (see Fig. 39, p 99). Such photos are not often published today, perhaps with good reason.

Power Rating and Sensitivity

The maximum power rating varies considerably between speakers and often a minimum power requirement is quoted as well. The rating is governed almost entirely by those of the drivers, so it starts with the choice of these. The driver rating indicates the maximum power it will handle, but this does not indicate the ultimate volume level. It may need a high power to produce a relatively moderate sound pressure if the enclosure design has sacrificed sensitivity for other parameters.

Alternatively, a highly efficient enclosure such as a folded horn would need a fraction of the power to produce a high output, and so would require only modestly rated drivers. The amount of acoustic power required varies with the listening room, a large one needs more than a small one, and a room heavily furnished with thick curtains, well-padded chairs and deep carpetting needs more than a sparely furnished one. High power then does not necessarily mean high volume.

The rating is thus linked with sensitivity, which is usually specified as a given dB level at 1 metre on axis for an input of 1 watt. Sometimes a voltage of 2.83 V is quoted instead of 1 watt. This is the voltage which produces 1 watt of power across an 8 – ohm load, however, the speaker impedance varies considerably with frequency so this is not a very reliable rating.

A speaker with a low sensitivity would have an output of around 80 dB, whereas one with high sensitivity would be 90 dB or more. Other levels at other distances can be easily calculated from this. To increase the level by 3 dB, the power must be doubled, so the difference in power required from 80 dB to 90 dB is over 8 times. A sensitive speaker at 5 watts can therefore give the same output as an insensitive one at 40 watts.

A sealed box loudspeaker behaves as a monopole sound source at all wavelength greater than its own dimensions, and for such a source the sound pressure level drops 6 dB for each

113

doubling of distance from the source in the far field (over 1.m). So if you listen at about 2 metres from the speakers, the power must be increased by 6 dB to give the same level as at 1 metre, hence is four times the 1 metre level. This assumes no reflections from the room boundaries i.e. an acoustically dead room. In practice, reflections reduce the amount of power required to give a specified level.

A reasonable rule of thumb for assessing musical sound levels is that a symphony orchestra produces about 90 dB when playing full fortissimo as heard from a good seat in a concert hall having good accoustics. For most of the time it is much less than this, and is also less in the loud passages when the performance is given in a theatre, where the sound is absorbed by curtains and drapes.

So for a speaker of average sensitivity producing 87 dB for 1 watt at 1 metre, we need to double the power to produce 90 dB, then quadruple it to give 90 dB at 2 metres. The power requirement is thus 8 watts from both channels or an average of 4 watts each in a dead room. For a normal room the power requirement would be less, probably threequarters of this, say 3 watts. For a low sensitivity speaker of 81dB for 1 watt at 1 metre, the power needs to be quadrupled to give the same results, so requiring 12 watts per channel.

These figures give no safety margin and should be at least doubled preferably trebled, to ensure that the amplifier and speakers are not overloaded on peaks and are working well within their linear range. So for a speaker of average sensitivity, 6 to 9 watts per channel should be adequate, while an insensitive model would need 24 to 36 watts.

At further distances in a normal room there is little reduction in sound pressure level because the free field at which the level falls 6 dB for a doubling of distance, is reinforced by the reverberent field in which the level is fairly uniform. No further increase in power is therefore needed.

For those who like rock music blasted at over 90 dB, double the power for each extra 3 dB and do not be surprised when your hearing above 4 kHz disappears before you are 40! These figures are approximate as much depends on the size and

114

furnishing of the listening room as well as the type of music reproduced and listening level preferences. However, it is evident that many systems tend to be overpowered.

Impedance

When a loudspeaker cone operates at its resonant frequency its excursion is greater for a given input than at all other frequencies. The back EMF is likewise greater and so less forward current flows. According to Ohm's Law as applied to impedance $Z = E/I$, so a reduction in current means a higher impedance.

An impedance graph is often published with loudspeaker specifications, which shows its value over the speaker's frequency range, and quite a lot can be learned from it (Fig. 40). Firstly a peak can be seen of some $25-40\ \Omega$ in the bass register. This is the main bass cone resonance and shows that even if the acoustic output is damped to give a flat response, the cone still makes large excursions at that frequency.

If the peak is very high, say over $50\ \Omega$, this indicates that the resonance is insufficiently damped and a peak in the output is likely. No doubt this has been engineered by the makers to give an apparently good bass response, but the result is really to make it boomy. This ploy is more likely to be found in bookshelf speakers in which bass would normally be deficient.

A lower peak of around $20\ \Omega$ or less indicates a well-damped resonance likely having a smooth roll-off, hence a more natural bass sound. This is usually found only in the larger enclosures.

Twin small peaks either side of the resonant frequency tell us that the enclosure is a reflex. These are really the sides of a resonance peak the tip of which is inverted by the restraining action of the resonating body of air in the exit port (see Fig. 24, p 65).

From the bass region the impedance rises toward the mid-frequencies where what appears to be a large peak is seen. This rise is not due to increased cone motion, but is the result of the increasing reactance of the coil. We remember that the reactance of an inductor increases with frequency, and the coil is of course inductive.

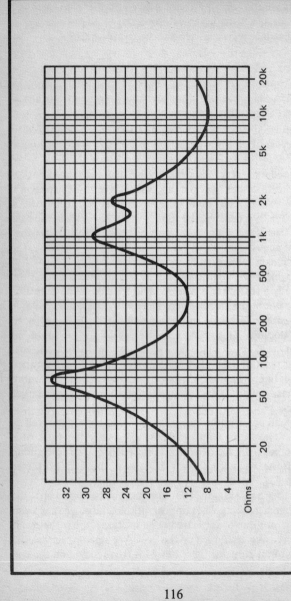

Fig. 40. Typical impedance chart for an infinite baffle enclosure. The 1st. peak is the effect of bass cone resonance; second and third due to the reactance of the tweeter taking over from the bass unit.

The peak is not due to any resonance but merely the fact that the bass driver is here fading out of the picture and the tweeter is taking over. At these frequencies the impedance of the tweeter coil is at the nominal 8 Ω, so the impedance curve descends to about this value, thus producing the peak at around the crossover frequency. Beyond this, the reactance of the tweeter coil rises with the increasing frequency so causing the curve to bend upwards again.

Sometimes the plot above the bass peak does not swing up but remains fairly flat. This indicates that the bass unit is already out of the picture due to a low crossover, which suggests the presence of a mid-range unit.

There may be other humps and dips due to the effect of the crossover network so that the overall impedance curve is quite complex. At any point over the whole range though, it should not fall to below 6.4 Ω otherwise the amplifier may be overloaded.

The curve complexity is a further reason why the design of a crossover network is so difficult and is individual to a specific set of drivers and enclosure. The basic circuits assume a fixed impedance, but the actual impedance curve is far from it.

Distortion

Many factors can contribute to distortion in the driver: cone behaviour, coil-end windings passing out of the main magnetic field at maximum excursion, uneven magnetic field distribution and non-linear compliance of the cone suspension. All these are under the control of the driver designer and there is little the speaker builder can do about them, much has to be taken on trust.

Causes of distortion that are under the control of the speaker builder are the crossover network, doppler distortion, and non-linear air load in infinite baffle enclosures.

That caused by the crossover depends on the actual circuit and its reflected effect on the amplifier. It is compounded by phase distortion between the two drivers and as we saw in the last chapter is a complex matter. It obviously can be avoided by not using one.

Doppler distortion is proportional to cone velocity at bass frequencies. It is therefore greater with smaller cones because they have to work harder to produce the same volume as larger ones. Resonance peaks in infinite baffle enclosures produce large cone velocities even when damped to give a flat acoustic output, and when only lightly damped the velocity is even greater. So, a single small speaker in an infinite baffle enclosure may produce detectable doppler distortion when driven hard. It is unlikely to be detectable in others, especially reflex and to a lesser extent transmission line enclosures, in which the resonance peak is heavily damped. The use of single full-range speakers should thus not be rejected because of the possibility of audible doppler distortion.

The non-linear air load in the infinite baffle enclosure is a source of harmonic distortion especially with the smaller enclosure. It has its effect when the half wavelength exceeds the longest dimension of the enclosure, so it appears at low frequencies. Over the majority of the mid and treble range harmonic distortion is usually under 1% but in the bass region can rise to 8%. The effect is also experienced with reflex enclosures.

It follows from this and also the practice of underdamping the bass resonance with small enclosures, that a good clean bass sound is virtually impossible with a small enclosure although it may apparantly produce a good bass response. If small overall size is imperative the infinite baffle is the only contender, and so the lack of bass definition must be accepted. There is a possible solution though which we will explore in the next chapter.

Chapter 7

KAPELLMEISTER DESIGN BRIEF

As pointed out in the last chapter, it is not yet possible to build a perfect loudspeaker, each design must be according to a set of particular priorities, and people differ as to what they consider the most important parameters. The Kapellmeisters were designed with certain definite priorities in mind; if these happen to be in accord with your own, the Kapellmeisters can be strongly recommended. The design was first published in *Electronics Today International*.

The first and rather discouraging restriction, which was forced by necessity, was that of size. Space was severely limited, so the size had to be kept down. Measuring the available wall space having due regard to all the other necessary furnishings revealed that the only space available for the width of each speaker was an unpromising 8 inches.

However, depth was less restricted and so was height, so if maximum air volume was to be achieved, the result had to be in the shape of a narrow column. This is not ideal for an infinite baffle speaker owing to the pipe-like behaviour of such a shape but perhaps a different type of enclosure could be engineered into that shape.

Natural uncoloured reproduction in the bass and in fact all registers was a high priority, but it did not seem attainable in view of the size limitation. However, an extended frequency response was not high on the list. Up to 15 kHz in the treble and down to 45 Hz in the bass was considered acceptable for the reasons outlined in the last chapter. Certainly undistorted bass was rated more highly than having lots of it!

Having established that, it did not take long to throw out the idea of a multi-driver speaker with a crossover network and all the phase and other distortions they generate. Instead, a single well-designed full-range driver was decided on. To reduce doppler and intermodulation distortion that are produced by large cone excursions at bass frequencies though, the driver needed to have a fairly large cone area so as to obtain the maximum acoustic output for the minimum cone excursion.

With a maximum width of 8 inches which must include the thickness of the sides, a large cone seemed impossible, but a reasonable area was in fact achieved by using an elliptical driver 5-inches by 8-inches mounted vertically.

There are two bonuses that arise from this: one is that a narrow cone and enclosure give a wide dispersion of high frequencies and an enhanced stereo effect, the other is that the single elliptical driver occupies less space than a multiple system. This is not only helps with the space problem, but simplifies construction and makes an alternative enclosure type to the infinite baffle feasible.

High power was given a low priority. Volume levels in excess of those heard in the concert hall with a full orchestra were considered unnecessary, in fact undesirable. Elimination of the crossover with its often-needed level balancing resistors meant fewer losses and higher sensitivity thereby permitting high acoustic output from low power. The drivers chosen are rated at 8 watts, and in the Kapellmeisters they produce well over 90 dB from a 4 watt per channel amplifer. A bonus here is that a truly hi-fi class A amplifier can be used as these can be easily designed to give low powers. It is high power operation at class A that produce the problems.

The problem remained as to which type of enclosure. The infinite baffle was not regarded with much favour because of the inherent non-linear air load distortion and resonance hang-over effects which both serve to distort the bass. These too are accentuated with smaller enclosures.

A transmission line was felt to be highly desirable but impractical because of the size and shape. But before abandoning the idea, a deeper investigation was decided on to see if any way could be found around the practical problems.

Conventional designs usually house all the drivers in a cubicle which extends to the back of the enclosure. From there the path, considerably reduced in area descends to follow its course through horizontal and vertical sections. A wave can be reflected from the rear of the cubicle back to the drivers just as in an infinite baffle enclosure, and so upset the smooth progression of the pressure wave along the transmission line. Other disturbances can occur at the bends with some back reflections, and storage and release of energy by the panels facing the bend thus producing coloration. Ideally, the transmission line should have no bends for this reason, although this really is a practical impossibility.

Furthermore, the line should be of the same area throughout to prevent unequal pressures along its length. Actual designs usually taper the line in an attempt to broaden and flatten the resonance peak introduced by each section.

By using a single driver, the cubicle can be dispensed with and the transmission line can start immediately from the speaker. Thus the back reflection is eliminated and the sudden decrease in area from the cubicle to the start of the first section. It also saves a lot of space.

If the bends could be eliminated, or more practically, if they could be designed to afford an almost perfect reflection of sound around them, the line would behave as it should, as one long pipe rather than a collection of small pipes each with its own resonance. Then the single resonance and its harmonics could be dealt with, tapering would be unnecessary, and the line area could be maintained throughout its length at its ideal optimum, which is the same area as the driver cone.

The whole thing can be thus be seen to hinge around the near-perfect reflection of sound around the bends. Some form of deflector placed at the correct angle at each bend is called for, but wooden panels are not the answer. They vibrate, store energy and release it, and are not perfect reflectors.

One of the best materials for reflecting sound is concrete, which it does some ten times better than thick wood. The only improvement on this is when the concrete is faced with highly glazed ceramic tiles. (Notice how the sound bounces around at a swimming bath.) If two tile-faced concrete wedges are arranged at a 45° angle even a U-bend can be negotiated, something which would be inviting trouble in a transmission line of conventional design.

The design thus materialised as a transmission line in three sections, one behind the other, each 33 inches (83.8 cm) long and having ceramic and concrete reflectors at the two U-bends (Fig. 41). This arrangement satisfied the minimum width requirement of 8 inches, while taking advantage of the less

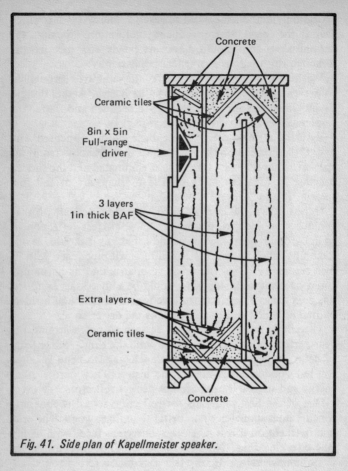

Concrete

Ceramic tiles

8in x 5in
Full-range
driver

3 layers
1in thick BAF

Extra layers

Ceramic tiles

Concrete

Fig. 41. Side plan of Kapellmeister speaker.

stringent restriction on depth. Actual depth of the completed Kapellmeister is 11 inches (27.94 cm), which although greater than the width is by no means large. The height puts speaker centre at 2ft 6ins (76.2 cm) above the floor which is just about at head level when seated in a reclining chair.

The exit vent is at the rear facing downward, so the speaker is supported on three small legs some 2 inches above the floor to allow what remains of the rear wave to escape. In addition to the length of the line which is over 8 ft, the distance from the vent to the front of the cone is at least a further 3 ft, making a total distance of over 11 ft. Thus no cancellation can occur at any frequency higher than that having a wavelength of 22 ft which is 50Hz, however the rear wave is so attenuated having travelled through 8 ft of absorbent material, that little cancellation occurs anyway.

The tiles are set at an angle of 45° to reflect the sound accurately around the bends. It will be noticed in the illustration that there is also a concrete and title wedge at the top just above the driver. The purpose of this is to reflect sound generated by the top part of the cone, downward.

The wave-front radiated by the back of a loudspeaker cone travels outward along an axis that is perpendicular to the surface of the cone. If the cone is at an angle of 22° which it is for the specified driver, the tile should be set at an angle of 56°. If the speaker has a different angle from this, the difference for the angle of the title should be halved, so a 20° angle cone should have a tile angle of 55°. Most loudspeakers of this size have cone angles in this region, but the angle varies slightly with cone curvative anyway, so the above figure can be used in most cases and is not too critical.

As the sound pressure on either side of the baffles is almost the same they are not excited into vibration to produce coloration, and this is true also of the back. The top and bottom pieces are of stout timber lined on their insides with the concrete and tiles, so they too are prevented from vibrating. Only the front panel has a sound pressure differential between its internal and external faces but this is much lower than with a totally enclosed cabinet. Also its narrow width makes for high rigidity which inhibits vibration. The structure of the enclosure thereby adds very little coloration to the sound.

Closed Pipe

The transmission line is as we have seen, a pipe that is closed at one end but open at the other. As such it exhibits a fundamental resonance plus odd harmonics; there are no even harmonics. The fundamental resonance occurs where the total length equals a quarter wavelength of the frequency. Here, the length is just over 8 feet, so the resonance is at 35Hz, which is below the lower frequency limit of the driver at 45 Hz. However, being broadened by the dampening material in the pipe, it can influence the range of the speaker usefully extending it below 40 Hz.

The antinodes (points of maximum air motion) at the third harmonic occur at the third and two-thirds positions, that is at the bends. Extra wadding at these points serve to suppress this harmonic. Extending the extra wadding up the first channel to the fifth position, and also at the exit, dampens two out of the three antinodes of the fifth harmonic. Above the fifth, the harmonics are smaller and the normal wadding fitted throughout the length of the pipe virtually tames these.

The specified speaker unit is the Altai 8553 DU, an 8 x 5 inch full-range elliptical which allowing for the frame and surround, has a 7 x 4 inch cone. Thus the approximate area is 22 sq.ins, while the area of the channels is 7 x 3 inch rectangular, which at 21 sq. ins is almost the same. The area remains constant right to the exit vent. A high frequency horn is fitted at the apex of the cone to improve the high-frequency efficiency and the response is 45 Hz − 16 kHz, a little better than the response decided in the brief. Resonant frequency is 50 Hz, and the power rating is 8 watts rms.

Parameters of the driver are not too critical, so if the specified one is not available any similar unit will do. The size is important, and this includes the front to back measurement which should be about $2\frac{1}{2}$ inches, (63.5 cm). It should be a full-range speaker with a response from 45 Hz to 15 kHz or better. Generally you will find that an extension at one end is at the expense of the other. High power is not essential because of the good acoustic and electrical efficiency, but 8 watts rms minimum, the same as the specified unit, is recommended. General good quality construction with a magnet of not less than 9,000 gauss, and a foam or similar surround should be looked for.

Chapter 8

BUILDING THE KAPELLMEISTERS

Most transmission line enclosures involve a lot of tricky woodwork so that many speaker builders with only modest woodworking skills are deterred. With the Kapellmeisters, although quite a lot of woodworking is needed, none of it is difficult, mostly it consists of cutting straight edges. These MUST be straight though, so if your saw cuts tend to wander, get the timber yard to cut them for you. The measurements are uniform with many pieces being identical; this helps a lot in the preparation.

Use standard 8 x 4-inch ceramic tiles, cut down to 7 x 4 inches. That is just one straight cut per tile. The exception is the top tile over the speaker which because of its different angle must be narrower, 7 x 3½ inches.

Triangular blocks are used to support the tiles as shown. These are made by first cutting 4, 3-inch squares, then sawing diagonally to give 8 triangles. The two blocks for the over-speaker tile are made by halving a 3 x 2-inch rectangle. A standard 3 x 1 mix of sand and cement is used to fill the space behind the tiles. In some cases the cement is applied first between the blocks and the tile bedded on to it, but in others the tile is fixed first to the blocks and the cement applied at the back afterward.

In all cases screw two or three stout screws at random angles into the wood where the cement is to be laid leaving about an inch out of the wood, so that they will be buried in the cement. These will then secure the concrete block in place when it is dry. Thoroughly wet the back of the tile before applying it to the cement. In some cases the front of the tile may need to be held in place while the cement sets, with panel pins knocked into the wooden sides. It does no harm to leave them there afterward.

All jointing is done by a strong wood glue. Evostik wood glue was used for the prototypes which is very strong and convenient to apply. It also fills any small gaps where the saw might have made a slight error. If not available, a substitute

125

will have to be used, but make sure it is a wood glue not a general purpose adhesive. Construction must proceed in numerous stages to allow the glue and concrete to set before continuing with the next, so some patience must be exercised. Make both speakers at the same time so that each stage can be completed on both and thus save time.

First Stage

First, consult the diagram of wood panels (Fig. 42), and buy sufficient plywood for all. Remember that these are for ONE speaker, so each will have to be duplicated. As so many are just 3 inch strips, it is likely that much can be obtained as off-cuts. Most large timber merchants sell these at a reduced rate, and the colour or grade doesn't matter as all are concealed except the top and bottom cheeks. The thickness should be as specified, $\frac{3}{8}$ths for the sides, baffles and back, $\frac{1}{2}$ inch for the front, and $\frac{1}{4}$ inch for the cheeks. It really will save a lot of time and energy if you get the merchant to cut the pieces with his machine saw.

He probably will not do the shaped lugs at one end of the baffles and bottom cheek, but this can be managed with a fret saw. It is the most difficult part, except the elliptical hole for the speaker, and fortunately, if the cut is a bit rough it doesn't matter very much. A $7\frac{1}{2}$ x $4\frac{1}{2}$ elliptical speaker hole should be cut in the front panel starting $2\frac{1}{4}$ inches from the top. It is desirable though not essential for the hole to be bevelled outward.

Second Stage

Having cut the pieces, we start with the front panel. Lay it face downward supported on some scrap quarter-inch ply or hardboard. Glue the top and bottom edges and fit the top and bottom boards. The front edges of these should NOT rest on the ply supports but directly on the work surface; they will thus protrude a quarter of an inch beyond the panel. They should also be positioned to give an equal overlap at either side. The idea is for the top and bottom cheeks to overhang the front, sides and back.

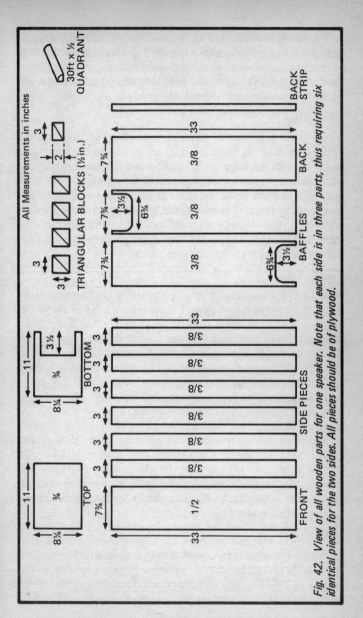

Fig. 42. View of all wooden parts for one speaker. Note that each side is in three parts, thus requiring six identical pieces for the two sides. All pieces should be of plywood.

127

Weights should be applied to the free sides of the cheeks to hold them against the panel while drying. Measure the distance between the rear edges of the top and bottom cheeks to ensure that it is exactly 33 inches and therefore the top and bottom are parallel. Wait for glue to set and harden.

Third Stage

Next, fit the first pair of side pieces, glueing the ends and the edge contacting the back of the front panel; ensure the pieces are flush with the edge of the front panel. Measure across the upper edges to make sure they are $7\frac{3}{4}$ inches and so are true. Now glue the triangular blocks in place at the bottom and top as shown in (a) of Figure 43, the top ones being the special sized ones. Glue the edges as well as the face that contacts the sides, but be careful in pressing them into place that you do not move the sides. Wait for the glue to set.

Fourth Stage

Now fit the speaker, screwing it place over the aperture, and connect by soldering, a pair of wires which are run down the panel to a hole drilled in the bottom. Leave a few inches free, and make sure both speakers are connected the same way to the colour-coded wire. It is prudent to cover the front of the speaker with a piece of card secured by drawing pins to protect the cone during subsequent operations.

Fit several screws to the bottom and top cheeks between the triangular blocks, leaving about an inch protruding at different angles. These will be embedded in the concrete when it is applied and so will hold the resulting concrete wedge in place. Next fill the space between the bottom blocks with cement (not too wet) and bed the tile onto it. Place the top narrow tile on the blocks and fill in behind it with cement. Allow time to harden; if desired a quick-drying additive can be used to speed matters up.

Fifth Stage

Saw suitable lengths of quadrant and glue into the corners between the front panel and the sides. It they are warped they should be held in place with panel pins. Glue two further strips of quadrant at the top inside edge of the sides and pin to secure.

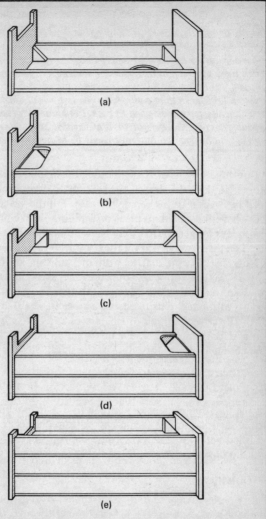

Fig. 43. (a) First stage in construction. The front is glued to top and bottom cheeks, using ¼ in supports to lift front into correct position. First pair of side pieces fitted and triangular blocks (small ones at the top) in position. Apply concrete, fit tiles and lay wadding.

129

Cut three lengths of BAF wadding to size and lay them in the cabinet so that two start at the bottom of the speaker, and the third lies over it to the top of the case. Fill the space above the speaker with a rolled up piece of wadding. Make the lengths a few inches longer so that they bend up at the bottom over the tile. The three layers will fill the channel without compression.

Now fit the first baffle with the cut-out at the bottom, glueing to the top edge of both the sides and the upper quadrant surface. Also glue to the top and bottom cheeks. Secure with panel pins to ensure a close fit as (b) in Figure 43. Next, fit the second pair of side pieces and two pairs of blocks top and bottom, (see c). Fit quadrant to corners as with the first channel, also to top edges of the sides; wait for all the glue to dry.

Sixth Stage

Fit the tiles and cement as with the first pair, not forgetting to fit the securing screws to top and bottom cheeks in the area to be filled with concrete. This time the top one will be bedded and the bottom one rear-filled. Wait for concrete to set.

Seventh Stage

Cut two pieces of wadding about 18 inches long and push half the length of each up the lower channel through the cut-out, and lay the other half length back along the top channel. Now lay three full length strips over these along the complete upper channel. This gives the extra density at the first bend needed to dampen the third harmonic antinode.

Next comes the second baffle which is glued and pinned as the first but with its cut-out at the top as shown at (d). Fit the third and final pair of sides, also the last pair of blocks plus the quadrant in the corners and top edges, see (e). Allow glue to harden,

Eighth Stage

Now for the last tile, again not forgetting the screws in the top to secure the concrete wedge. Mount the tile on the blocks using panel pins to keep it in place; this will be easier if the enclosure is stood vertically upside down. Return to the horizontal, and fill in rear with cement. Wait until set.

Ninth Stage

Lay three strips of wadding in the channel making sure the bend is filled. Put some extra here if necessary to fill completely. Cut another strip about 24 inches long and tuck half the length under the other three at the outlet, and bring it over the top so that it covers the rough ends. Lastly glue and pin the back in place.

Tenth Stage

Now for the finishing. Sand down any ridges in the sides, but do not be too fussy, for they will be completely covered with fabric. Check carefully for any cracks or crevices in the jointing and fill with the wood glue. Sand, then stain or varnish the top cheek and the edges of the bottom one, there is no need to do underneath unless you are fussy. Paint the body with matt black including the inside rim of the loudspeaker aperture, but be very careful not to get any paint on the loudspeaker cone as this would affect its flexibility. The painting ensures that the bare wood does not show through the fabric with which the whole body excluding the cheeks is covered.

The two back strips (one for each speaker) should now be cut to fit exactly between the top and bottom cheek rear overhangs. These strips conceal the join in the fabric covering so should be about $\frac{3}{4}$ inch to one inch wide preferably bevelled

131

at both edges to give a good finish. They should be stained or varnished the same colour as the cheeks.

Eleventh Stage

Obtain sufficient black speaker fabric to cover both speakers. Any other colour can of course be used if preferred and is obtainable.

Cut the fabric to the exact size to cover the body between the cheek overhangs, but leave a flap 4 inches longer and 8 – inches wide, at the start. Secure the vertical starting edge at one edge of the back of the enclosure with tacks so that the flap hangs over the bottom. Then pull it around, keeping it taut, overlapping the start and securing it with one of the wooden strips down the middle of the back. This can be done with brass countersunk screws with cupped washers which give a professional-looking effect.

Next trim the flap to fit between the prongs of the bottom and fix it across the exit port with gimp pins.

Twelfth Stage

Make a pair of 2-inch high legs similar to those shown in the side-view illustration in the last chapter. A single rear one should be made to incline backward under the rear exit vent to give greater stability as in the illustration. They can be stained or varnished to match the rest. Pack filler around the hole in the bottom through which the speaker wire passes to make it airtight, and fit a connecting block underneath.

The Kapellmeisters are now complete and ready to go into action. So what sort of performance can be expected? Technical and listening tests were made on the prototypes and the following section describes the results.

Performance

As an anechoic room was not available, frequency response tests were made by means of the multiple microphone position technique. They were repeated on the second speaker in a different position, and the results were very close, so the plot reproduced here can be considered accurate (Fig. 44).

132

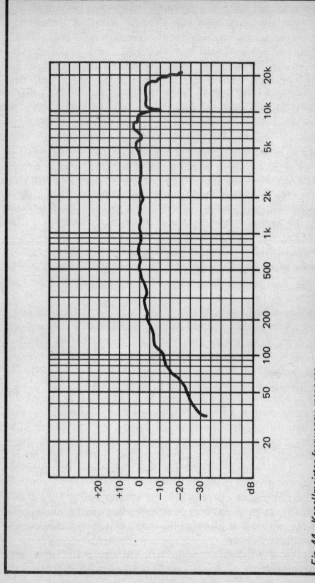

Fig. 44. Kapellmeister frequency response.

Surprisingly, the treble response is sustained beyond 16 kHz and actually continues up to 20 kHz, a remarkable achievement for a single driver speaker with no tweeter. This is a tribute to the controlled flexure of the cone and the effectiveness of the high-frequency horn. The undulations are fairly smooth, and some of the vicious peaks and dips encountered with certain multi-driver speakers are notably absent. The response is within 5 dB from 16 kHz to 200 Hz, apart from small deviations at 7 kHz and 10 kHz, There are of course no phase problems over any part of the range.

As expected, the bass is not sustained with a flat response to as low a frequency as would be obtained from a large infinite baffle or reflex enclosure. The response crosses the − 5dB level at 200 Hz and from there a very gentle descent, but audible output is maintained down to around 36 Hz, which is lower than the design brief. Actually, there is a 3 dB drop in the octave 500 − 250 Hz, a 6 dB drop from 250 − 125 Hz, and a 12 dB drop from 125 − 62 Hz and below.

This gentle and gradually increasing slope results in a more natural and musical bass than when the roll-off is lower, but steeper. A further advantage is that this curve is ideal for applying a little bass boost at the amplifier. All bass boost controls hinge the response curve upward from a pivotal point at 1 kHz. Frequencies just below 1 kHz are hardly affected, but the amount of boost increases as the frequency drops. If bass is boosted with speakers having a steep roll-off, the frequencies just above the roll-off point are lifted to produce a hump, so resulting in a boomy effect. Here, bass boost will lift the curve to give a flatter response without boom.

Thus with a little boost in the bass, the single driver in an enclosure only 8 inches wide can be made to give a response equivalent to that of a much larger multi-driver speaker, but without the phasing problems and distortions they and the crossover network produce.

The impedance curve is also of interest and is here shown (Fig. 45). There is no large peak in the bass, just a small rise at 100 Hz, which is at the third harmonic of the transmission line resonant frequency.

Bass peaks indicate a high back EMF generated by a large cone movement at the resonant frequency, even though the

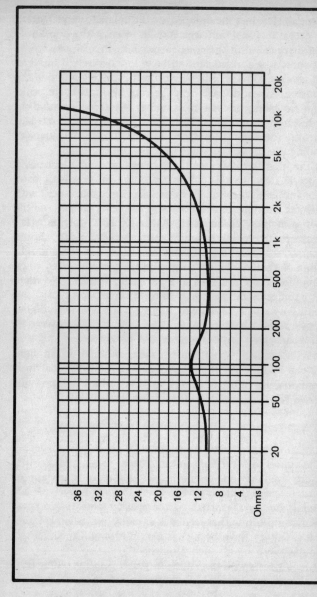

Fig. 45. Kapellmeister impedance chart.

acoustic output may be damped by the cabinet design. Often these excursions may be large enough to enter the non-linear region or even strain the cone suspension. In such cases bass boost should be applied cautiously and moderately if at all to avoid speaker damage, quite apart from causing a hump in the response as noted above. Here, having no impedance peak, there is no excessive cone excursion at any frequency and no such restraint is necessary. Bass boost can thus be applied to obtain a satisfactory balance without fear of damage, providing the speaker's power rating is not exceeded.

At the high frequency end, the impedance curve gradually rises to 60 Ω at 20 kHz. This is not due to increasing cone movement but the increase of the coil reactance with frequency. This means that less power is being taken from the amplifier at these frequencies. As amplifier distortion often decreases with an increase of load impedance, this should present a very 'easy' load for any amplifier, and there should be none of the unexpected problems often encountered when an amplifier takes a dislike to a particular speaker. Nowhere does the impedance fall below 10 Ω

Sensitivity is 90 dB for 1 watt input at 1 metre. This is higher than average and enables an amplifier of just a few watts to be used. Five watts per channel should be sufficient and well within the speaker's eight watts rating, although up to eight watts can be used for the larger listening room. This affords the opportunity to use a class A amplifier which can easily be designed for low powers such as these.

Listening Tests

Technical measurements can tell us a lot about how a speaker should sound, but they are not infallible. Some speakers that measure well sound dreadful, while others that appear unexceptional in the tests perform very well subjectively. Much of this is due to the effect of the speaker and its crossover network on the amplifier feedback circuits, unpredictable until you actually try them both together. With the Kapellmeisters of course there are no such problems

Listening tests with the Kapellmeisters operating with a little bass boost confirmed all hopes. The results are not 'spectacular', so those looking for thump, blast and tizz would be disappointed. Instead, musical instruments sound as if they *are* musical instruments. Nonetheless there is plenty to excite the ear in full-blooded orchestral climaxes.

Ambience and sense of presence was perhaps the first noticeable effect, Woodwind was clear, easily identifiable and rounded in tone. Brass was brilliant yet mellow, stacatto passages really were stacatto, not slurred as they sometimes sound. A recording of a harpischord was astonishing, revealing tones and subtleties never heard before, it really sounded as if was right there between the two speakers. A solo violin sounded natural with no moments of discomfort in the higher passages. One passage in an orchestral work that always sounded as if it was performed by the 'cellos playing pizzicato, could be clearly identified as played on the lower registers of a harp. 'Cellos sang, not grunted and rasped. Many recordings were really heard for the first time.

The coherent phasing and narrow sound source had their expected effect on stereo imaging. An unconventional instrumental positioning employed by a renowned foreign orchestra was instantly noticed during a stereo broadcast. Stereo broadcast drama proved quite dramatic, with positive locational identification even in crowd scenes.

The 'hole-in-the-middle' effect whereby all the sound comes either from the left or the right and none from in between, is often obtained when the listener is too close to the line between a pair of speakers. This has not been experienced at all. In fact, listening actually on the line with the speakers on either side produces a rock-steady central image apparantly right in front of the listener's face. As with most speakers the most consistent stereo effects are produced with the speakers turned slightly inward.

There are a couple of drawbacks though. One is that after becoming accustomed to the Kapellmeisters most other speakers sound rather boxy or muddy in comparison, so they rather spoil one's enjoyment of music when heard on other systems!

The other snag experienced was that a large collection of recordings that formerly were considered acceptable, soon became divided into those that were really excellent, those that were reasonable, and many that were poor. The excellent qualities of the first group and the bad ones of the last had been concealed by the previous speakers. In common with all good speakers, the Kapellmeisters show up faults in the programme material as well as bringing out the best in it. So be prepared to replace some of your recordings.

How Much Bass Boost?

As noted previously the response is improved with a little bass boost, but not too much. It is not easy to make an accurate adjustment with music; with the price of concert seats as they are, few of us are all that familiar with the real thing.

A better test is something we hear every day, the human voice, and in particular the female voice. Why female? Because we naturally expect bass sounds in a male voice so if we apply too much bass it may not be noticed. Tune to a f.m. radio station broadcasting a female voice, then advance the bass control slowly from the flat position. The first effect is a fuller tone which sounds pleasing and natural, but soon bass 'chesty' tones will be heard which are not. Turn the control back a point from here and you will have the optimum position. Having established this you will find it gives the most natural effect with the male voice and music, thereby confirming the setting.

Treble Boost

Treble boost should not be needed unless you have thick carpetting, plenty of well-padded furniture and in particular a large area of curtaining. The latter is the factor having the greatest effect. Even then, boosting should be very limited as too much gives a hard tone which may seem bright and crisp to start with but soon produces uncomfortable moments and listening fatigue. The Kapellmeisters need very little, if at all.

Paradoxically, the best test is the male voice, which contrary to popular expectation, has more high-frequency content than the female. The reason is that although the female has a higher

138

fundamental tone it is purer, with fewer harmonics than the average male.

Tune to a broadcast of a male speaker and listen for the consonantal sounds ch, t, d and s. Slowly advance the treble until these are heard distinctly, but naturally with no exaggeration. Any tendancy to lisp shows you have gone too far.

Blank Page

Index

A

B

C

NOTES